THE W
CAN T

CW00420168

THE WORLD OF CAN THEMBA

Selected writings of the late Can Themba

Edited by Essop Patel

Published by Ravan Press (Pty) Ltd
PO Box 31134, Braamfontein, 2017 South Africa

First impression 1985
Second impression 1988
Third impression 1990

Cover art: Mzwakhe Nhlabatsi
Design: The Graphic Equalizer
Typesetting: Sandy Parker

ISBN 0 86975 145 X

Printed and bound by Galvin & Sales, Cape Town
(6732)

ACKNOWLEDGEMENTS

The editor and publisher would like to thank the following for permission to use material in compiling the selected writings of the late Can Themba:

— Jim Bailey and *Drum* for *Mob Passion; Forbidden Love; Passionate Stranger; The Nice Time Girl; Marta; The Urchin; Terror in the Trains; Inside Dube Hostel; Why Our Living's So Tough; World's Longest Walk to Work!; Girls in High-Heel Shoes; Russian Famo Sesh!; Boozers, Beware of Barberton!; Our Hungry Children; Nude Pass Parade; Zeerust: What the Men Say About It; Let the People Drink!; Dinokana, The Target; O Ghana; Ballad to the Coffee Cart; Your Man's Been Clapped . . .; Y-Yes, Darling; I Couldn't;* Five parts of *The Life and Love of Dolly Rathebe; Zeke Past Bachelor of Arts! Casey Past Bachelor of Hearts!; Henry Nxumalo* and *Music, Food of Love.*

— The Classic Magazine Trust Fund and *The Classic* for *The Suit; Dear God* and *The Boy with the Tennis Racket.*

— The proprietors of *Africa South* for *The Bottom of the Bottle* and *Requiem for Sophiatown.*

— Faber and Faber Ltd., Ellis Ayitch Komey and Ezekiel Mphahlele for *The Dube Train.*

— Anne, the widow of the late Can Themba for *The Will to Die* and *Ten-to-Ten.*

CONTENTS

PREFACE

We were these sensitive might-have-beens who had knocked at the door of white civilization (at the highest levels that South Africa could offer) and had heard a gruff 'No' or a 'Yes' so shaky and insincere that we withdrew our snail horns at once.

Can Themba   (From 'The Bottom of the Bottle')

The creative and artistic impulse in a fragmented society often comes from the ghetto rather than from the affluent strata of society. This assertion is substantiated by the vitality of the Sophiatown Renaissance of the Fifties and the volume of black writing in South Africa today. In the last three decades a torrent of black creativity has emerged from the townships. From the early days of Sophiatown to the present there has been a distinct township culture manifested in music, in the visual arts, in drama and in literature. A culture of self-assertion, it has been both virulent and dynamic. The aspiring black writer is seldom surrounded by volumes of belles-lettres; instead he is in the midst of human conditions and experiences — hunger, misery, deprivation and lurking fear. These are the raw materials of art which the black writer confronts; like the blacksmith, he must forge the story, the poem, the song or the painting. The artist cannot remain aloof from the mainstream of the life of the people. According to Lewis Nkosi ' . . . the poet or the artist in general is there to *celebrate* his own or his society's sense of being . . . and not there to subvert its values or moral order. The artist in Africa is a man alienated neither from his community nor the world of Nature which sustains him.'

Born in Marabastad in 1924, Can Themba was at the centre of the Sophiatown Renaissance. As a young man of precocious talent, he won the first Mendi Memorial Scholarship to study at the University of Fort Hare. In 1947 he graduated with a first class degree in English and later returned to the university to read for a University Education Diploma. Before Can Themba emerged as a writer he taught at the Madibane High School in Western township (see Stan Motjuwadi's recollection) and subsequently at the Johannesburg Indian High School in Fordsburg.

Can Themba's first attempt at short story writing, 'Mob Passion', won him the first prize in the *Drum* short story competition in 1953. At the time he said, ' . . . I feel inspired to go on writing and writing, until one day, perhaps, I'll be a really famous author.' This launched Can on a new career. He started out as a journalist for *Drum* and *Golden City Post,* and he was associate editor of both in turn. We can probably accept Motjuwadi's verdict that this self-confessed 'corrosive cynic' was 'no leg man'. His journalism always leaned towards literature, and this volume of his selected writings is a memorial to his versatility.

In 1963 Can Themba, alias D'Orsay Can Themba or Can von Themba, with his family, went into exile in Swaziland. In 1968 he died in Manzini. At the time of his death tributes flowed in from fellow writers and former colleagues. Stanley Motjuwadi wrote: 'Can was more interested in people than in politics. When a man with a large family was arrested for a political offence, unlike other editors, he was more interested in the human story of the stranded family.' And Harry Mashabela said, 'Can was over-complex. A rebel. A man of the people. A kind of genius. A rascal. Nonsensical. All crammed up in one man. And yet he remained something of a legend. As a rebel he scorned convention, tradition, custom, and loathed authority. But as a man of the people, he liked at the very bottom of life, mixing with the lowly and doing precisely what he felt was the right thing to do.'

I am particularly indebted to Ravan Press from whom came the initial enthusiasm for the idea of compiling and editing these selected writings of the late Can Themba. I would also like to thank Mothobi Mutloatse for his encouragement and Anne, the widow of the late author, for her approval and consent to make this book possible. Much appreciated is the patience and sacrifice of my wife, Khatija and my sons 'the Pats'. Today they are too young to understand why this volume was imperative; I hope one day they will learn that men like Can Themba searched and laboured to make a meaningful South Africa for them. My sons will discover that Can Themba, like Nat Nakasa, sacrificed himself for the people. They had no real business to die so young!

Essop Patel
JOHANNESBURG

THE MAN FROM THE HOUSE OF TRUTH
A Recollection of Can Themba

Talk had gone the rounds at Madibane High at Western Township that we would be getting a new teacher from Fort Hare who had obtained his B.A. with a distinction in English. As black matriculants grappling with irrelevant guys like Shakespeare, Milton and the vagaries of English poetry we felt that any black getting a distinction in English at university must be something out of this world. A phenomenon.

You can imagine our disappointment when the principal Mr Harry Madibane proudly stood on the stage and introduced the new wonderboy. He was scrawny with an incongruously puffy, rubbery face. At my most generous, I would not say he looked a 'bit' distinguished. Sartorially he was a disaster. No tie, a cheap baggy grey workman's gaberdine trousers, a khaki shirt, shoes that had an overdue date with the repairers and the kind of jacket a fussy student would not be seen dead in. Quite a let down after the imposing figure we had over the days built up in our minds.

Fortunately our disappointment was short-lived. From the moment he opened his mouth to address us, we were, to use a cliché, eating out of his bony palm. Blinking all the time like something unused to harsh lights, he spoke in a cool, sophisticated voice. He used words we were accustomed to, but he used them the way only he could. Eloquent and articulate, he really made the occasion his show without being pompous. On the contrary, he made us feel like his equals.

This was my first encounter with Can D'Orsay

Themba.

Can was to disappoint me once more. Although he didn't teach us, our own English teacher had a great respect for him. So before we sat for our final exams, he asked Can to test us in essay writing. He gave us the subject, 'The Poetry of the Earth Is Never Silent'.

I went all out to please the man from Fort Hare, pulling out all the stops.

When the scripts came back, the first thing I looked for was Can's remarks at the end of what I regarded as my magnum opus.

'The poetry of your earth is ever silent,' was Can's verdict. Can, however, more than made up for it a few years later when he asked me to join him on *Post* where he was news editor and later assistant editor.

To be invited by Can, who was rated among the top black writers, was for me like being granted the freedom of the city.

In spite of the respect and awe he was held in as a writer, Can proved to be the most prosaic person I'd ever met. At lunchtime he would send to the Chinaman around the corner for pork bones and some slices of bread.

It may sound a bit unAfrican for me to be referring to someone older than me — and my former teacher at that — by his first name, but Can in his own vain manner had an answer for this. As he used to say: 'Have you ever heard of Mr Jesus, or Mr Shakespeare?

Can loved company and he was superb company himself. A sparkling conversationalist with razor-sharp repartee. But what stands out in my mind is the day editor Arthur Rudolph found Can snoring on his desk, dead drunk. Arthur warned Can that the next time he found him drunk on the job he would fire him. Can lifted his head, looked at Arthur through bleary eyes.

'Yes, promises, promises, promises. That's all a guy can get in this place,' Can slurred, dropped his head once more on the desk and continued with his snoring.

Until he met his charming wife Can never discriminated in the kind of girl he fancied. Once I had to object when he came along touting a tatty scrubber.

'Voetsek,' he said. 'Who am I to question what the gods give.'

At the time he had a pad in Sophiatown we called The House of Truth. The place perhaps was Can's way of cocking a snook at snobbery, officialdom and anything that smacked of the formal. Everybody but the snob was welcome at The House of Truth. You did not have to have permission to bunk with your date on the only single bed in the room. Can would stagger in in the early hours of the morning and pass out in a corner on the floor.

Can was vain. But his was the kind of healthy, innocent vanity of a child. Like the time he rushed up to my desk with a hardcover book.

'Look!' He showed me the index of the book. There were the names of well-known writers.

'And look here.' There was the name, Can Themba.

'Yes boy, at last immortality has caught up with me.' He gave that laugh of his that rocked his disjointed frame.

Although the Writers Association of South Africa honoured him with the Henry Nxumalo Award for his contribution to journalism, Can was never a leg man. For him, slogging it out in search of news bordered on the mundane. He was essentially a writer.

He fell four-square on the definition of a poet as somebody who can give to airy nothing a local habitation and a name. Yes, Can could write about nothing and anything and make it pleasant reading.

Like one day when Sir Tom Hopkinson, former editor of *Drum*, approached the chief sub. 'Look, I don't know what Can is writing about. I don't know what he is trying to say but it is mighty good prose. We must use it,' he said.

Can was an erratic genius. He had many faults but at times he reminded me of a song we used to sing as kids at Sunday school. 'Look them up. Get them gone. All the little rabbits in the field of corn. Anger, envy, jealousy, pride. These must never in my heart abide.'

Can never had any of these rabbits.

Stan Motjuwadi

PART ONE

Short Stories

MOB PASSION

There was a thick crowd on Platform Two, rushing for the 'All Stations' Randfontein train. Men, women and children were pushing madly to board the train. They were heaving and pressing, elbows in faces, bundles bursting, weak ones kneaded. Even at the opposite side people were balancing precariously to escape being shoved off the platform. Here and there deft fingers were exploring unwary pockets. Somewhere an outraged dignity was shrieking stridently, vilely cursing someone's parentage. The carriages became fuller and fuller. With a jerk the electric train moved out of the station.

'Whew!' sighed Linga Sakwe. He gathered his few parcels upon his lap, pressing his elbows to his side pockets. He did not really have any valuables in these pockets; only long habit was working instinctively now.

Linga was a tall, slender fellow, more man than boy. He was not particularly handsome; but he had those tense eyes of the young student who was ever inwardly protesting against some wrong or other. In fact at the moment he was not a student at all. He

was working for a firm of lawyers in Market Street.
He hoped to save enough money in a year or two to
return to university to complete an arts degree which
he had been forced by 'circumstances' to abandon.

People were still heaving about in the train but
Linga was not annoyed. He knew that by the time
the train reached Langlaagte, or Westbury, most of
these folks would be gone and he would be able to
breathe again. At Braamfontein many people alighted;
but he was not thinking of his discomfort any more.
He was thinking of Mapula now. She had promised
that she would be in time for this train. That depended, of course, on whether she had succeeded in
persuading the staff nurse in charge of the ward in
which she worked to let her off early.

The train slowed down. Industria. Linga anxiously
looked outside. Sure enough, there she was! He gave
a wolf-whistle, as if he were admiring some girl he did
not know. She hurried to his carriage, stepped in and
sat beside him. They seemed not to know each other
from Adam. An old man nearby was giving a lively
account, in the grimmest terms, of the murders
committed in Newclare.

At Westbury the atmosphere was tense. Everybody
crowded at the windows to see. Everywhere there
were white policemen, heavily armed. The situation
was 'under control', but everyone knew that in the
soul of almost every being in this area raved a seething
madness, wild and passionate, with the causes lying
deep. No cursory measures could remedy; no super-
ficial explanation could illuminate. These jovial faces
that could change into masks of bloodlust and
destruction without warning, with the smallest
provocation! There is a vicious technique faithfully
applied in these riots. Each morning these people

quietly rise, and with a business-like manner hurry to their work. Each evening they return to a Devil's Party, uncontrollably drawn into hideous orgies. Sometimes the violence would subside for weeks or months, and then suddenly would flare up at some unexpected spot, on some unexpected pretext.

At Newclare, too, from the train all seemed quiet. But Linga and Mapula knew the deceptive quiet meant the same even here. The train rushed on, emptier. Only when they had passed Maraisburg did these two venture to speak to each other. Linga was Xhosa and Mapula Sotho. A Letebele and a Russian! They had to be very careful! Love in its mysterious, often ill-starred ways had flung them together.

Linga spoke first.

'Sure you saw no one who might know you?' he asked softly.

'Eh-eh,' she replied.

She fidgeted uneasily with the strap of her handbag. His hand went out and closed over her fingers. They turned simultaneously to look at each other.

A sympathetic understanding came into Linga's eyes. He smiled.

'Rather tense, isn't it?' he said.

She looked past him through the window.

'Witpoortjie!' she exclaimed. 'Come, let's go.'

They rose and went to the door. The train stopped and they went out. Together they walked to a bridge, went over the line and out by a little gate. For some two hundred yards they walked over flat, stubbly ground. Then they went down a mountain-cleft at the bottom of which ran a streamlet. They found a shady spot and sat down on the green grass. Then suddenly they fled into each other's arms like frightened children. The time-old ritual, ancient almost as

the hills, always novel as the ever-changing skies.
For a long time they clung to each other silently. Only
the little stream gurgled its nonsense; these two daring
hearts were lost to each other. The world, too —
good, bad or indifferent — was forgotten in the
glorious flux of their souls meeting and mingling.

At last Mapula spoke — half cried:

'Oh, Linga! I'm afraid.'

'Here where the world is quiet?' he quoted, with
infinite softness. 'No, dear, nothing can reach and
harm us here.' Then with a sigh; 'Still, the cruellest
thing they do is to drive two young people like guilty
things to sneak off only to see each other. What is
wrong with our people, Mapula?'

She did not answer. He lay musing for a long time.
She could see that he was slowly getting angry. Sometimes she wished she could understand the strange
indignations of his spirit and the great arguments by
which he explained life. Most times she only yearned
for his love.

'They do not see! They do not see!' he continued
vehemently. 'They butcher one another, and they
seem to like it. Where there should be brotherhood
and love, there are bitter animosities. Where there
should be co-operation in common adversity, there
are barriers of hostility, steeling a brother's heart
against a brother's misery. Sometimes, 'Pule, I understand it. We have had so many dishonest leaders, and
we have so often had our true leaders left in the lurch
by weak-kneed colleagues and lukewarm followers,
that no one wishes to stick his neck out too far.
Where is the courage to weld these suicidal factions
into a nation? The trouble is, very few of us have a
vision comprehensive enough of our destiny! I believe
God has a few of us to whom He whispers in the ear!

Our true history is before us, for we yet have to build, to create, to achieve. Our very oppression is the flower of opportunity. If not for History's Grand Finale, why then does God hold us back? Hell! and here we are, feuding in God's dressing-room even before the curtain rises. Oh! — ' He covered his face and fell into her lap, unable to say any more.

Instinctively Mapula fingered his hair. In God's dressing-room, she thought. What does it mean? But his anguish stabbed at her heart. Trying to forget herself, she only sought within her a tenderness to quell the bitter wretchedness she had heard in his voice.

'Linga, no! Let me show you something else — something that I understand. It is not so long before you and I can marry, I dream about the home that we are going to have. I . . . I want that home, Linga. You taught me that woman's greatest contribution to civilisation so far has been to furnish homes where great men and great ideas have developed. Moreover, there's our problem. Let us rather think of ways of handling my father. No, no; not now. Let us think about the present, about *now.*'

Thabo was running faster now that he was nearing home. His mind was in a whirl; but he knew that he had to tell his father. The lop-sided gate was in the far corner, so he smartly leaped over the fence where it was slack. He stopped abruptly at the door. He always did when there were people. But now he soon realised these people were his two uncles — Uncle Alpheus and Uncle Frans. Somehow great news always brings a glory of prestige on the head of the bringer. Thabo felt himself almost a hero now; for these two men were die-hard stalwarts in the Russian

cause. Uncle Alpheus was a romantic firebrand while
Uncle Frans was a scheming character of the power-
behind-the-throne variety. They were complementary
to each other: together a formidable team.

'Father, where is he?' hissed Thabo, breathing
hard. The excitement in his voice aroused everyone.

'Holy Shepherd! What's the matter, boy?' cried
Uncle Alpheus.

'Mapula, Mapula. She loves with a Letebele.'

'What!' exploded Uncle Alpheus. 'Where is she?'
Then more calmly: 'Come'n, boy. Tell us everything
more quietly; your father is out there?'

'J-J-Jonas t-t-tells me — J-Jonas is a boy who works
with me — Jonas tells me that Mapula loves with a
Letebele. They always meet at the hospital; but never
in the sitting room. He hopes to marry her.'

'Never!' barked Alpheus. Just then the door burst
open. A party of men carried in the limp form of
Thabo's father. He was unconscious and blood
streamed all over his face. Beyond them, just outside
the door, a crowd had gathered. Everyone was at
once asking what had happened. As the news spread,
ugly moods swept the crowd. Ra-Thabo was carried
into the bedroom and tended by the women. Alpheus
and Frans returned to the fore-room and conferred.

'What now?' Alpheus asked Frans.

'Of course, we must revenge. You will talk to the
people — the women. Talk fire into them. Connect it
with the Mapula business; that'll warm them. Suggest
drugs — a Letebele must use drugs, mustn't he? I'll be
in the house. Just when they begin to get excited I'll
arrange to carry Ra-Thabo out — to the hospital, you
know. See if we can't get them bad!' He smiled cheer-
lessly.

Outside, the crowd — mostly women — was thickening. Even in the streets they could be seen coming along in groups, blanketed men and women. From the house Thabo and his little sister, Martha, joined the crowd. It was obvious that their uncles were going to do something about it.

Alpheus stepped onto the little mud wall. He raised his left hand and the blanket over it rose with it. This movement was most dramatic. In a few moments the crowd moved closer to him and became silent. Then he began to speak. He began in a matter-of-fact voice, giving the bare fact that Ra-Thabo, their leader had been hurt. Warming gradually he discussed the virtues of this man. Then he went on to tell of how this man had actually been hurt. Neither confused fighting nor cowardly brutalities rose in the mind as this man spoke, but a glorious picture of crusaders charging on in a holy cause behind their lion-hearted leader. Oh, what a clash there was! The Matabele were pushed beyond Westbury station. There the heroes met a rested, reinforced enemy. For a moment all that could be seen was the head of Ra-Thabo going down among them. The clang of battle could be heard; the furious charge could be seen, in the words of this man who was not there. The Baso-thos fought desperately and won so much ground that their all but lost leader could be rescued and carried back home. And what finds he there? Alpheus's voice went down softer and heavier, touching strings of pathos, rousing tragic emotions which the hearts present had never before experienced. There was an automatic movement in the crowd as everybody strained forward to hear. In awful, horror-filled whispers he told of Ra-Thabo's daughter giving herself to a Letebele. The thing is not possible! he hissed. It would not have happened if the maid had not been bewitched with drugs. Are they going to brook it! he cracked. No! all the throats roared. Are they ready for vengeance! Now! thundered the mob. Someone in the crowd shouted *'Mule!'* Then the women took up their famous war-cry, chilling to a stranger, but driving the last doubting spirit there to frenzy and fury.

Ee!-le!-le!-le!-le!-le!-le!-Eu! Eu! Eu!

Now they were prancing and swaying in uninterpretable rhythms. A possessed bard in their midst was chattering the praises of the dead, the living, and the unborn; his words clattering like the drumsticks of a fiend.

'Let us go past Maraisburg and attack them from the rear!' yelled Alpheus over the din.

At that moment the door of the house went open. The mob, which had been on the point of dashing out, recoiled. The sight they saw stunned them. Frans and two other men were carrying out Ra-Thabo, besmeared with blood. Thabo saw Uncle Alpheus leaping with trailing blanket and yelling 'To Maraisburg!' Again he leaped over the fence into the street. The mob followed hard on his heels.

'MULE!' 'MULE!' 'MULE!'

As the last blanket swept round the corner, Frans turned back to the injured man. His two helpers had also been drawn in by the irresistible suction of the mob-feeling. With a smile he said to the unhearing Ra-Thabo: 'I'll have to get a taxi to take you to hospital, brother.' Then he carried him back into the house.

Late in the afternoon the train from Randfontein suddenly stopped at Maraisburg. Everybody was surprised. Something must be wrong. This train never stopped at Maraisburg. Then suddenly!

'All Change! All Change!' And more brusquely:
'Come'n. *Puma! Puma!'*

Linga and Mapula hurried out. News had arrived
that trouble had started again at Newclare; more
seriously than usual. All trains from Randfontein
were being stopped here and sent back.

Shrugging, Linga drew Mapula away, and arm-in-
arm they strolled along the platform, out by the little
gate, into some suburban area. For a time they
walked on in silence. Then Mapula spoke.

'I hope I'll get back in time,' she said.

'Then let's walk faster. We might get a lift outside
the suburb.' They walked into the open country.
Linga knew that if he could only find a certain golf-
course somewhere around here, he would know
where the road was. Meanwhile, they had to stumble
on over rough country, and Mapula's cork-heeled
shoes were tormenting her toes. She limped on as
stoically as she could. Linga did not notice her
suffering as he was looking out for familiar land-
marks. Those trees looked suspiciously like the golf-
course to him.

When they reached the trees Mapula said: 'Linga
let us rest here; my toes are suffering.'

'All right,' he replied. 'But I must look for the road.
Let's look for a cool place where you may rest while
I search for the golf-course.'

'Mm.'

He led her amongst the trees. She sat down and
pulled off her shoes. When he thought he saw a
shadow of distress flit across her brow he bent down,
took her hand, pressed it and muttered: 'Back in a
moment, sweet.' He rose slowly, looked at her
indecisively, then turned away slowly and walked off.

He did not search far before he noticed a torn and

faded flag. The hole was nearby. Suddenly he emerged
from the cluster of trees, and came upon the road.
But his attention was caught by a horde of Russians
pursuing a woman who came flying towards Linga.
This spelt trouble for the Letebele. But in a flash he
thought of an idea. He spoke fluent Sesotho and
believed he could pass for a Mosotho, possibly as
a Russian. He quickly drew a white handkerchief
from the pocket of his trousers, tied it round his
head. This made him look like an active supporter
of the Russian cause. Skirts flying, the woman sped
past him. Facing the mob he shouted:

'Helele!'

All its wrath spent, the mob crowded round out of
sheer curiosity. Some were even in a jocular mood
now; one playing lustily on a concertina. But here
and there Linga could see deadly weapons snatched
up in their hasty exodus from Newclare. He spoke to
them in fluent Sesotho, taking his idiom from Teya-
teyaneng. He asked if he was on the road to Newclare;
he said that he worked in Roodepoort, but was going
to Newclare because his uncle there wanted more
man-power in the house. Won't they please tell him
where this road was?

'Che! It is no Letebele this; this is a child of at
home,' remarked Alpheus.

'Kgele! You speak it, man,' said a burly fellow.
Then everyone directed Linga to Newclare.

Just then Mapula came running, shoes in hand and
stockings twisted round her neck.

'Linga! Linga, my darling! What are they doing to
you!' she screamed as she forced her way through
the crowd. Linga stiffened. When she reached him
she flung her arm around him and clung to him with
all her strength, crying all the time. Then she saw her

uncle, stupefied like the rest of them, standing there. She ran to him and begged him to save her lover. He pushed her aside, walked up to Linga, and stood before him, arms akimbo.

'Ehe! So you *are* a Letebele after all. You lie so sleekly that I can understand why my daughter thinks she loves you.' Then he swung round, his blanket trailing in an arc. 'Friends, we need go no further. This is the dog that bewitched my brother's child. Let's waste no time with him. Tear him to pieces!' The mob rushed upon Linga: '*Mmate! Mmate!*'

'Uncle! Uncle!' cried Mapula. But even as she cried she knew that nothing could be done. She had courted the contempt of her people; and she understood now that all her entreaties were falling upon deaf ears. Whether from convenience or superstition — it did not signify which — she was considered the victim of the Letebele's root-craft.

Suddenly from the scuffling mob flew an axe which fell at her feet. In a flash she knew her fate. Love, frustrated beyond bearing, bent her mind to the horrible deed.

Mapula acted. Quickly she picked up the axe whilst the mob was withdrawing from its prey, several of them spattered with blood. With the axe in her hand Mapula pressed through them until she reached the inner, sparser group. She saw Alpheus spitting upon Linga's battered body. He turned with a guttural cackle — He-he-he! He-he-he! — into the descending axe. It sank into his neck and down he went. She stepped on his chest and pulled out the axe. The blood gushed out all over her face and clothes. With that evil-looking countenance she gradually turned to the stunned crowd, half lifting the axe and walking slowly but menacingly towards the largest group.

They retreated — a hundred and twenty men and women retreated before this devil-possessed woman with the ghastly appearance. But then she saw the mangled body of the man she loved and her nerve snapped. The axe slipped from her hand and she dropped on Linga's body, crying piteously:

'Jo-o! Jo-o! Jo-o! Jo-na-jo! Jo-na-jo!'

Someone came and lifted her up. Someone else was dragging Alpheus's bleeding corpse by the collar so that his shoes sprang out one after the other.

The crowd was going back now. All the bravado gone, they were quiet and sulky. Only the agonised wailing of Mapula could be heard. Every breast was quelled by a sense of something deeply wrong, a sense of outrage. The tumult in every heart, feeling individually now, was a human protest insistently seeking expression, and then that persistent wail of the anguished girl, torturing the innermost core of even the rudest conscience there. The men felt themselves before God; the women heard the denunciations of thwarted love. Within they were all crying bitterly:

'Jo-o! Jo-o! Jo-nana-jo!'

FORBIDDEN LOVE

Dora Randolph was now running in the dark, down the road that dipped into the hollow of the bridge spanning the stream that separated Noordgesig from the Western areas. From the bridge the road climbed the hillock and sailed away to Newclare, Western Township and Sophiatown.

He must have seen her for his dark form swam towards her, and caught her in his strong arms.

'Not here, darling,' he said hastily, 'some carlights may strike upon us.'

He led her higher up the road into the tall grass. Suddenly she caught his coat lapels and dragged him down so that no one could see them. He clambered towards her and curled her into his arms. His lips thrilled upon hers, burningly sweet, and with digging fingertips she tried to find the source of his fire in his spinal column.

Then the flames went out of them, settling into a low glow. She broke away with a sigh. She caught a stalk, put it in her mouth, and turned to look at the scattered lights of Noordgesig.

'They were at it again, Sweetie,' she said between

her teeth, 'and what makes me mad is that I cannot fight back anymore.'

'What did they say now?' Mike asked, a little worried.

'Mr Van Vuuren was at our place again. It looked almost as if Dad had called him in to preach to us. He spoke about how terribly important it is that we keep away from the 'Natives', otherwise we would be associated with them. And his voice had a trick of making that word 'associated' sound horrible. But what made me hate him was the way he stared at Louisa as he spoke. I —'

'Louisa is that sister of yours who is dark, isn't she?' Michael Chabakeng asked. He had seen her once at the Rhythmic Cinema with Dora, and he remembered how she was darker even than he, and that she had woolly, kinky hair like his.

Dora went on: 'Yes, the dark one, and I feel like giving back to them all the hurt that they make little Louisa suffer. Why wasn't it I, Mike? Why wasn't I dark, instead of fair? Then you might not have been so afraid of my love?'

'Huh?' Michael was so taken aback by the sudden tenseness in her tone that he did not quite know what to say.

She turned her head and placed her chin on to his chest. 'Somehow, Mike,' she tried to explain, softened again now. 'I feel trapped by a doubly guilty shame. I am ashamed that it is my people who are in the forefront of every move against your people — ashamed of my father whom I love, but who is violent in his hatred of Africans; ashamed of my sister Louisa, who ought to feel nearer your people, but hates them so unreasonably; ashamed of my brother's shame for having been classified African; ashamed of my mother's silence when I suspect (I know it!) that she disapproves of their attitudes. And then, Sweetie, sometimes when I listen to them all, I — I — I am ashamed, in a queer way that I hate, of this secret love of ours. Oh!'

Michael drew her close, and then his voice came, softly as if it came out of the grass: 'I don't know if I can make you understand this. But, darling, everybody's trouble is that he is afraid. *Everybody!* Even you and I.

'Your father, and that . . . that Mr Van Vuuren are afraid their old world is turning over and they will now have to fight for things. And they are not used to fighting. They have too long . . . too long . . .' he searched frantically for words that would not hurt her, and at last said weakly, 'too long not fought.'

'Yes, Mike,' she said.

'Your sister, Louisa, is afraid because of this thing that might tear her away from you — all who she loves, and from the comparative safety of your way of life; this thing, this business of becoming an African is nearest to her, seems would soonest catch her in its cruel fingers. More than the fear of your father and Mr Van Vuuren, hers is most likely to become cruel.'

Michael thought about what he was saying for a moment. The significance of his own words was only just becoming clear even to himself.

'But my mother, Mike, I can't understand her silence.'

'I'm not sure I can understand everybody's fear,' Michael said after a moment, 'but, tell me, haven't you ever felt that your mother chooses silence because she doesn't want to say anything that might influence her children?'

'I see, Mike,' Dora said, feeling with her fingers for the hard swelling on his biceps. 'And my fear is that I know I'm doing just the thing that my mother fears her words might influence us into doing.'

'Partly. But, my dear, let's forget all the world's fear. Let's forget even your fear and mine. Between you and I, there is, lying side by side with the fear, a faith. Let's feed the faith. Let's talk of love.'

'No, Sweetie, let's not talk of love, let's just lie still in each other's arms, and feel it.'

After a long while he released her, raised her to her feet. 'Tomorrow, three o'clock show at the Rhythmic. Here's your ticket.' He kissed her again.

The headlights of a car on a bend higher up shone on them for a moment. A ghost-like shadow flew out to Noordgesig like a tongue flicked out of a mouth mockingly.

As the driver of the car dipped into the bowl towards the river and the bridge, he said to his companions: 'That guy sure must have a dangerous weapon.'

In their two-room apartment in Sophiatown Michael was again nagging his sister about the one thing that was eating into his peace of mind.

'You keep stalling, dodging me, but do you think it is really in the best interests of the child that you hide its name? After all, I've been thinking of getting married myself . . . sometime soon . . . ' and his voice trailed off.

'Don't you worry, Mike,' Salome said. 'I've the child's true interests at heart. But there are times when there is good reason for not doing the obvious thing. I assure you the child's father is an honourable man. That is all I can say for the moment. You must trust me.'

Michael looked into the fire in the stove, his mouth twisted into a strained grimace of concentrated thinking.

'I still don't like it,' he said at length. 'What about you, what about your future? However romantic, I don't like the picture of a man who will not stand up to his responsibilities.'

'You don't understand.' And she began to hum one of those catchy songs that fill the streets of Sophiatown now and then for a brief spell.

Michael felt beaten again. He was always beaten in this game. The trouble was that he had full confidence in his sister's intelligence. But this, she was right, he could not understand. He remembered something he had heard somewhere: 'A woman in love is operating at the lowest level of the intellect.' He went out.

Meneer Carelse of the Noordgesig Primary School, leaned over the gate of the school yard and looked for the small group of coloured boys who would be sitting in a circle in a corner of the yard. He called one of them.

'Take my bag and put it into the History classroom,' he said to the sandy-haired, smart-looking youngster who came up to him. He looked at the circle of boys wistfully. He knew what they were doing now during these precious few minutes before lessons started. They were teasing each other in the age-old school tradition. Probably vulgar, the naughty little scamps, he thought tolerantly as his mind went back to his own school-days as a youngster. Then he hurried away to Aunt Sannie's house for that daily cup of coffee.

Meanwhile Freddie Williams, the sandy-haired, smart-looking youngster sped across the playground to the History classroom. Freddie was not going to miss that morning's session of their little tease-club. But gee! they got Bobby Randolph at last. Freddie had met Dick Peters that morning on their way to school, and that eternal victim of Bobby Randolph's tease-tongue had intimated to Freddie that he had a bombshell with which he was going to blow Bobby to bits and blazes. That is why, as he went flying over the playground, Freddie had shouted to the gang already assembled, 'Wait for me!'

Dick Peters did wait for Freddie. He wanted a full audience, and he wanted to make sure that his friend Freddie was present in case of any fighting.

Freddie was still gasping for breath when Dick stood up, faced Bobby, and exploded his bombshell without finesse or ceremony.

'Your sissy goes with a Naytif!'

'You lie!'

'Yes, it's true. I seen her by the bioscope on Saturday. Your sissy goes with a Naytif!'

The gang burst into laughter. Bobby broke loose with such a fierce barrage of blows upon Dick that they both tumbled over onto the ground. Dick did not stand a chance. Bobby's arms were flailing into his face and the blood was spurting out. Dick yelled out with sudden fear and pain.

Meneer Carelse had to push aside the cheering youngsters before he could get at the rolling fighters. He pulled Bobby off and held the two apart.

'What're you fighting for?'

'He hit me first,' Dick said, inconsequently.

'Why did you hit him, Bobby?'

'He says my sister goes with a Naytif.'

'It's true,' Dick shouted. 'I seen them myself on Saturday by the bioscope.'

For a moment Meneer Carelse was stunned by the news. Through his mind rushed with painful vividness the picture of his proposal of marriage to Dora Randolph and the disdainful rejection she had given him. He could see again her lip curling up in contempt. He knew . . . he had always known, that she rejected him because of his drinking habits that were notorious in the township but he felt too deeply hurt to admit his weakness.

Suddenly his own lip curled up as a malicious thought darted through his mind.

'To the head you go, both of you,' he said as he dragged them away.

After Mr Phillips had taken in the whole story he sent the youngsters off, asking them to report back to him at half-past one when the school dismissed. He told Meneer Carelse to wait a moment as he wanted to talk to him.

'Meneer,' began the head with a pained expression in his eyes, 'it is our duty to hush up the whole cruel affair. You know, we could handle the youngsters, and the matter need not go further than this school.'

'But . . . but . . . . '

'Yes?'

'But, I think we owe it to the girl's family to tell them of the danger their daughter is putting them in.' Meneer Carelse was most sanctimonious.

Mr Phillips stared at the lean man before him long and hard before he spoke.

'Of course, our interest is just for the good and safety of the family. We do not have,' — with deep emphasis — 'any desire to do them harm. It would not somehow mysteriously happen to be that the whole world knows of it.'

'Really, I must say!' was all Meneer Carelse could manage.

Then both men stared silently out of the window. It was a long minute before Mr Phillips could say, 'That will be all, Meneer.'

But it did somehow mysteriously happen that the whole world came to know of it. Dora's disgrace was on everybody's lips. To everybody, except to Dora herself, this was disaster. She decided that it was release from the long months of stolen, forbidden love. And felt a thrill in defiance.

This of course gave added fuel to the wagging tongues. On the bus, within earshot of her father, one man was heard to remark, 'I learn the brazen hussy doesn't care at all. It just goes to show the government isn't exactly wrong in all cases that it reclassifies back to kaffir.'

Old man Randolph winced.

To restore some of the Randolph family honour Dora's brother, Davie, got together a few of his friends who solemnly pledged to put matters right: 'Just wait till we catch him.'

If Michael had seen the group of young coloured lads near the doorway of the Rhythmic Cinema that Saturday he would not have suspected a thing.

He had decided to take it easy with Dora since he had received her hurriedly scribbled note that the whole thing had cracked, despite her insistence that she 'didn't care a damn.' He had written her that for some time at least, if they wanted to go to the cinema they would have to go on separate occasions.

But this was a great picture, he had read about it in the papers and just had to see it. He knew that

Dora was going to be there, but he hoped she would understand.

At the cinema he saw a group of African fellows gesticulating and arguing heatedly with the manager. He went up to them and found to his annoyance that the film was banned for 'Children under twelve and Natives'.

Suddenly he heard a voice shouting, 'Aw, beat up the blurrie kaffirs!' As he swung round a coloured chap caught him by the shoulder and hit him on the mouth, cutting his upper lip.

'Davie don't!' came Dora's shriek from somewhere and Michael knew that he had had it.

She appeared before him and faced her brother.

His eyes opened wide. 'So this is the blurrie bastard! Hey, boys, this is Dora's kaffir!'

They ignored the other Africans who scampered away in all directions, and crowded in on Michael and Dora. Dora turned to Michael and in a fierce but reassuring whisper said, 'I'm with you in this to the end.'

As they closed in, Michael pushed Dora behind him, and faced Davie.

'Look, Davie boy,' he said tersely, 'take my advice and don't do it. I'm not scared of being beaten up, I'm scared of what this will mean. Take my advice, and don't do it.'

'Yefies!' said Davie, 'what does he think he can do — nothing!'

In a flash he kicked Michael in the stomach so that he doubled up. Someone caught hold of Dora and held her fast. The others jumped upon Michael and rained blows on him in a mad fury. He made no attempt to fight back. Only instinctively he protected his face as best he could. Someone blew a police whistle and the attackers dashed into the maze of byways and alleys of Fordsburg. Michael was out cold.

When he came to, Dora was weeping over him. He tried to lift himself but could not. She helped him up, still crying bitterly. Together they staggered to the bus-stop, off to Sophiatown.

At home Michael fainted again. So Dora had to explain to his sister what had happened. She introduced herself and began to relate the events exactly as they had happened.

A queer look of amusement came into Salome's face.

'Randolph? Randolph? Randolph you say? And your brother's name is Davie. David Randolph. I've got an idea. You stay here and as soon as Mike is well enough, we'll go and see old Davie, nê?'

For days Salome did not speak about the matter. The two women who loved Michael so much looked after him, nursed him back to health.

Then one Sunday morning Salome said suddenly, 'Look, you two, I think it's time we went to see old Davie. I want a little word with him.'

'Aw, cut it out, I don't want any more trouble,' said Michael.

'Oh no, there won't be trouble at all. Just a little talk,' Salome replied mysteriously.

Dora accompanied them to her home, her heart beating wildly. They found the whole family at lunch. Even Mr Van Vuuren was there philosophizing expansively.

Davie went pale when he saw the threesome walk in.

Before they could say anything Salome took over. 'Hello, Davie,' she began. 'Remember me? You beat up my brother because he's in love with your sister. Okay, now I've brought my brother to beat you up because you were in love with *his* sister. Fair enough?'

'You lie!' Davie said hoarsely.

'I thought you'd say that, so I brought some proof. Where do you suppose I got this handsome picture of yours, Davie? And just in case you deny that one too, I'd like your father to read these flaming letters you once wrote to me.'

She pushed a neatly-tied bundle of letters to the old man, saying tartly, 'And to think I treasured these letters because they came from the only man I ever loved.'

The old man seemed only then to be suddenly galvanized into life.

'Get out! Get out of my house!' he shrieked.

Salome kept cool.

'Oh no, you don't. If you get tough I'll take your son to court for not supporting his child for the last three years.' She turned to her brother. 'Mike, you've been asking me all the time who the father of my child was and I've been silent. I told you it's a man I love, a man who would come into the open if he could but that his circumstances were exceptional. You thought it was a married man. Well, that is the man!' — she pointed a trembling finger at Davie.

The family was stunned. Salome was now heaving with emotion.

The old man grabbed the packet of letters and said, 'You can't prove it.'

Salome laughed out, a hard, cruel laugh.

'There's one letter at home, the one in which your son begged me not to expose him.'

Then Dora's mother spoke out. 'My grandchild! I've got a grandchild! My God, I must see that child.'

Something in the old lady's voice calmed Salome.
'Yes, mother,' she said softly.

Michael and Dora walked out quietly. She looked
into his eyes and said: 'Somehow I think the fear will
fade away now.'

THE DUBE TRAIN

The morning was too cold for a summer morning, at least, to me, a child of the sun. But then on all Monday mornings I feel rotten and shivering, with a clogged feeling in the chest and a nauseous churning in the stomach. It debilitates my interest in the whole world around me.

The Dube Station, with the prospect of congested trains filled with sour-smelling humanity, did not improve my impression of a hostile life directing its malevolence plumb at me. Despairing thoughts of every kind darted through my mind: the lateness of the trains, the shoving savagery of the crowds, the grey aspect around me. Even the announcer over the loudspeaker gave confusing directions. I suppose it had something to do with the peculiar chemistry of the body on Monday morning. But for me all was wrong with the world.

Yet, by one of those flukes that occur in all routines, the train I caught was not full when it came. I usually try to avoid seats next to the door, but sometimes it cannot be helped. So it was on that Monday morning when I hopped into the Third Class carriage. As the train moved off, I leaned out of the paneless window and looked onto the leaden, lacklustre platform churning away beneath me like a fast conveyor belt.

Two or three yards away, a door had been broken and repaired with masonite so that it could no longer be opened. Moreover, near the door a seat was missing which transformed the area into a kind of hall.

I was sitting opposite a hulk of a man; his hugeness was obtrusive to the sight when you saw him, and to the mind when you looked away. His head tilted to one side in a half-drowsy position, with flaring nostrils and trembling lips. He looked like a kind of genie, pretending to sleep but watching your every nefarious intention. His chin was stubbled with crisp, little black barbs. The neck was thick and corded, and the enormous chest was a live barrel that heaved back and forth. The overall he wore was open almost down to the navel, and he seemed to have nothing else underneath. I stared, fascinated, at his large breasts with their winking, dark nipples.

With the rocking of the train as it rolled towards Phefeni Station, he swayed slightly this way and that, and now and then he lazily chanted a township ditty. The titillating bawdiness of the words incited no honour of lechery of significance. The words were words, the tune was just a tune.

Above and around him, the other passengers, looking Monday-bleared, had no enthusiasm about them. They were just like the lights of the carriage — dull, dreary, undramatic. Almost as if they, too, felt that they should not be alight during the day.

Phefeni Station rushed at us, with human faces blurring past. When the train stopped, in stepped a girl. She must have been a mere child. Not just *petite*,

but juvenile in structure. Yet her manner was all adult
as if she knew all about 'this sorry scheme of things
entire' and with a scornful toss relegated it. She had
the precocious features of the township girls, pert,
arrogant, live. There was that air about her that
petrified any grown-ups who might think of asking
for her seat. She sat next to me.

The train slid into Phomolong. Against the red-
brick waiting-room I saw a tsotsi lounging, for all the
world not a damn interested in taking the train, but
I knew the type, so I watched him in grim anticipation.
When the train started sailing out of the platform, he
turned round nonchalantly and trippled along backwards towards an open door. It amazes me no end
how these boys know exactly where the edge of the
platform comes when they run like that, backwards.
Just at the drop he caught the ledge of the train and
heaved himself in gracefully.

He swaggered towards us and stood between our
seats with his back to the outside, his arms gripping
the frame of the paneless window. He noticed the
girl and started teasing her. All township love-making
is rough.

'Hi, rubberneck!' — he clutched at her pear-like
breast jutting from her sweater — 'how long did you
think you'd duck me?'

She looked round in panic; at me, at the old lady
opposite her, at the hulk of a man opposite me. Then
she whimpered, 'Ah, *Au-boetie*, I don't even know
you.'

The tsotsi snarled, 'You don't know me, eh? You
don't know me when you're sitting with your student
friends. You don't know last night, too, *nê?* You
don't know how you ducked me?'

Some woman, reasonably out of reach, murmured,

'The children of today . . . ' in a drifting sort of way.

Mzimhlope, the dirty-white station.

The tsotsi turned round and looked out of the window on to the platform. He recognized some of his friends there and hailed them.

'O, Zigzagza, it's how there?'

'It's jewish!'

'*Hela*, Tholo, my ma hears me, I want that ten-'n-six!'

'Go get it in hell!'

'Weh, my sister, don't listen to that guy. Tell him Shakespeare nev'r said so!'

The gibberish exchange was all in exuberant superlatives.

The train left the platform in the echoes of its stridency. A washerwoman had just got shoved into it by ungallant males, bundle and all. People in the train made sympathetic noises, but too many passengers had seen too many tragedies to be rattled by this incident. They just remained bleared.

As the train approached New Canada, the confluence of the Orlando and the Dube train lines, I looked over the head of the girl next to me. It must have been a crazy engineer who had designed this crossing. The Orlando train comes from the right. It crosses the Dube train overhead just before we reach New Canada. But when it reaches the station it is on the right again, for the Johannesburg train enters extreme left. It is a curious kind of game.

Moreover, it has necessitated cutting the hill and building a bridge. But just this quirk of an engineer's imagination has left a spectacularly beautiful scene. After the drab, chocolate-box houses of the township, monotonously identical row upon row, this gash of man's imposition upon nature never fails to intrigue me.

Our caveman lover was still at the girl while people were changing from our train to the Westgate train in New Canada. The girl wanted to get off, but the tsotsi would not let her. When the train left the station, he gave her a vicious slap across the face so that her beret went flying. She flung a leg over me and rolled across my lap in her hurtling escape. The tsotsi followed, and as he passed me he reeled with the sway of the train.

To steady himself, he put a full paw in my face. It smelled sweaty-sour. Then he ploughed through the humanity of the train, after the girl. Men gave way shamelessly, but one woman would not take it. She burst into a spitfire tirade that whiplashed at the men.

'Lord, you call yourselves men, you poltroons! You let a small ruffian insult you. Fancy, he grabs at a girl in front of you — might be your daughter — this thing with the manner of a pig! If there were real men here, they'd pull his pants off and give him such a leathering he'd never sit down for a week. But, no, you let him do this here; tonight you'll let him do it in your homes. And all you do is whimper, "The children of today have never no respect!" Sies!'

The men winced. They said nothing, merely looked round at each other in shy embarrassment. But those barbed words had brought the little thug to a stop. He turned round, scowled at the woman, and with cold calculation cursed her anatomically, twisting his lips to give the word the full measure of its horror.

It was like the son of Ham finding a word for his awful discovery. It was like an impression that shuddered the throne of God Almighty. It was both a defilement and a defiance.

'*Hela,* you street urchin, that woman is your mother,' came the shrill voice of the big hulk of a man, who had all the time been sitting quietly opposite me, humming his lewd little township ditty. Now he moved towards where the tsotsi stood rooted.

There was menace in every swing of his clumsy movements, and the half-mumbled tune of his song sounded like under-breath cursing for all its calmness. The carriage froze into silence.

Suddenly, the woman shrieked and men scampered on to seats. The tsotsi had drawn a sheath-knife, and he faced the big man.

There is something odd that a knife does to various people in a crowd. Most women go into pointless clamour, sometimes even hugging fast the men who might fight for them. Some men make gangway, stampeding helter-skelter; but with that hulk of a man the sight of the gleaming blade in the tsotsi's hand, drove him berserk. The splashing people left a sort of arena. There was an evil leer in his eye, much as if he were experiencing satanic satisfaction.

Croesus Cemetery flashed past.

Seconds before the impact, the tsotsi lifted the blade and plunged it obliquely. Like an instinctive, predatory beast, he seemed to know exactly where the vulnerable jugular was and he aimed for it. The jerk of the train deflected his stroke, though, and the blade slit a long cleavage down the big man's open chest.

With a demoniacal scream, the big man reached out for the boy crudely, careless now of the blade that made another gash in his arm. He caught the boy by the upper arm with the left hand, and between the legs with the right, and lifted him bodily. Then he hurled him towards me. The flight went clean through the paneless window, and only a long cry trailed in the wake of the rushing train.

Suddenly passengers darted to the windows; the human missile was nowhere to be seen. It was not a fight proper, not a full-blown quarrel. It was just an incident in the morning Dube train.

The big man, bespattered with blood, got off at Langlaagte Station. Only after we had left the station did the stunned passengers break out into a caco-phony of chattering.

Odd, that no one expressed sympathy for the boy or the man. They were just greedily relishing the thrilling episode of the morning.

PASSIONATE STRANGER

Osbourne Ledwaba was bitter against his father for the way the old man had treated his friend, Reginald Tshayi, with whom he had come to Chebeng to spend a short vacation. Why did he call him a Jo'burg tsotsi? Surely it was rude! He stole a glance at Reggie who seemed unaffected by his father's rudeness.

'Reg,' began Osbourne, 'I'm sorry.'

'Nonsense, Ossie,' Reggie replied. 'Fathers are like that the world over.'

As he spoke, in came the most beautiful creature with a tray of tea-things. She put them down on the little table before saying 'hello' in the loveliest voice and with the sweetest smile.

Osbourne introduced her with obvious pride.

'This is Ellen, Reg. The prettiest sister anybody ever had! Kid, this is Reg. He teaches in a high school.'

'Glad to meet you. Your brother calls me a rag, but I've a real surname too. I'm Reginald Tshayi.'

'I hope you'll have a happy time with us. Please excuse me.' She floated out of the room.

Osbourne's father came in later and told Osbourne

that they should go to the chief's kraal to pay their
respects.

'Your friend needn't bother,' concluded the old
man.

'But . . . but . . . ' Osbourne complained.

'Don't worry, Osbourne,' Reggie came to the
rescue. 'This gives me a first-class chance to finish off
that last chapter of *Salome*.'

Osbourne left with his father. Reggie had hardly read
a few lines when there came a light tap on the door.
It was Ellen.

'Oh, reading?' She arched her brows so prettily. 'I
saw Osbourne and father leave, so I thought I might
invite you to join me in the sitting-room if you'd like
to.'

Reggie went with her. They talked about many
things, but inevitably he told her of Jo'burg. He did
not try to thrill her, but the sincerity and fervour of
his dissatisfaction spoke so vehemently that she
remarked:

'You needed this holiday badly, Reggie. You
know, you've a tremendous capacity for powerful emotion.' Then precipitatively: 'Tell me, have you
ever been in love?'

Reggie rose from his chair and sat down on the
floor in front of her. He looked up into her face
before he replied.

'Ellen, I *am* in love. I needed to escape the smoke
and filth, the misery and degradation of Jo'burg to
discover that something fresh and sweet is still
possible in womanhood. If my declaration sounds
premature and impetuous to you, forgive me. Love is
on the wing, and whether I will it or no, I must join
its flight. Whether I will it or no, I must love you.

Destiny itself has guided my wanderings to this far
place, that I may lay my troubles in your bosom.
Have I ever loved? you ask. How shall I say? There
have been those who scratched on the surface of my
life, but my soul has been virgin. Never before has my
soul echoed the resounding depths or soared the
giddy heights as now. What those wretched women in
Jo'burg with their earthly desires inspired in me was
retreat from the name of love. Now I know what true
love can mean. Never more can the stars whirl and
wheel the same, if you do not love me too, Ellen. No
more would the moon shed soft silver on the earth;
no more would the flowers gladden the heart, the
birds 'untune the sky'. O nevermore! I reach for your
lips knowing I reach for the sun.'

'Too soon, Reggie. It's too soon to be true!' Ellen
grasped him by the shoulder, pleading her fear.

'Two lives pre-ordained for each other, love treads
on the paths of the lightning. Whether we will it or
no, we must discover and fulfil each other.'

'Whether we will it or no,' Ellen whispered as she
sank down on his imploring lips.

They lay in each other's arms long and still, silently
contemplating this thing the gods had done. The first
storm of passion spent, a great peace descended on
them as soul met soul in perfect unity, and their
bodies intertwined like a woven whip. Deep meaning
suffused their union so that perfect understanding
was achieved. And they were one.

'Reggie! Reggie!'

'Mm.' He squirmed gently in the tangle of her
embrace, then lay still again.

'Reggie. Reggie, darling, father and Osbourne will
soon return. We must separate . . . and, Reggie, we

must keep our love secret,' she admonished. 'Father won't understand.'

'Tonight, after supper, under the big tree opposite the cattle-kraal. I'll be waiting for you.' All the eagerness of his new love was in his voice.

'I'll be there, darling,' she whispered.

He went to his room whilst she tried to tidy up the sitting-room. When Osbourne and his father returned, they were arguing heatedly.

Osbourne had discovered that his father was negotiating a marriage between Ellen and Dikgang, and he was filled with anger. Reggie had to intervene. He took Osbourne off and had a long talk with him. At supper Osbourne apologised to his father. He simply said, 'Father, I'm sorry.' The meal broke up in a tense atmosphere. Reggie and Osbourne went to their room.

'Drown yourself in your trumpet, Ossie,' Reggie said to him. 'I want to take a solitary walk and sort my ideas.'

Reggie slipped out into the night and casually strolled to the big tree near the cattle kraal. He did not wait long before Ellen came. He took her in his arms and they spiralled away into a heaven where their rebel emotions could harmonise. But earth is never far from heaven, for just then Ellen's father came upon them.

'Ha!' he started. 'Who are you? Ellen! What are — so it's the Jo'burg tsotsi already demonstrating Jo'burg behaviour. You come into my house, enjoy my hospitality, bewitch my son, and now you seek to seduce my daughter! Tomorrow you leave my house, and never let your shadow darken its threshold again.'

'If you say so, my father,' Ellen said. 'Tomorrow I

leave your house with him.' The sharp menace in her
voice startled him. 'It's useless trying to tell you I
love him. You wouldn't understand.'

'But what about Dikgang?'

'Go marry him yourself.'

'Get to your room! As for you, you . . . you . . . .'
The old man struck Reggie and spat, but Reggie did
not move a hair. Then the old man swung round in
impotent rage, caught Ellen by the arm and dragged
her to the house, with a thousand damns.

Back in the room, as Reggie was packing and Osbourne
was looking glumly on, the old man reappeared. He
looked wretched.

'Osbourne, I want you to come and talk sense into
your sister. She's packing her clothes . . . .'

'My father,' Osbourne interrupted quietly, almost
meekly, 'when I said this evening that I'm sorry, I
meant *I* at least had realised that Ellen's love-affairs
are not my business. And father, I'm going to pack
too.'

In his despair, the old man turned to Reggie.

'You can make them stay. I beg you to dissuade
them from their cruelty to their mother, and then go
quietly.'

Suddenly Reggie felt very tired. The note of pain
in the old man's voice sounded genuine; but his
interpretation of the situation was unfair, and the
implication of his demand terrible. Reggie was
trapped. Yet he was to be given no chance to decide.
Voices were heard outside, and the old man went out.
When he returned he was in a different mood. He was
light-hearted and gay, with a malicious gleam in his
eye, and a smirk of cruel joy on his lips.

'Osbourne,' he said, 'there'll be a meeting in the

sitting-room. I want you to be present. I want your
friend to be present too.'

'When, father?'

'Now.'

When Osbourne and Reggie came to the sitting-
room they found members of the Chief's Council
come to settle the question of Dikgang's bride-price
for Ellen. After the introductions a grey-headed old
man spoke: 'Well, Ledwaba, last time we discussed
this union, you virtually promised us your daughter if
the bride-price was right. We're instructed by the
Chief not to wrangle over the number of cattle. You
may, therefore, consider it settled at any number you
care to fix.'

'That speeds our discussions. Shall we say twenty-
five?' Old Ledwaba was happy with the turn of
events. He rubbed his hands affably.

'Father,' broke in Osbourne, unexpectedly, 'may I
say something?'

Ledwaba frowned and shifted uneasily. But before
he could say anything, the grey-headed old man said,
'Certainly, certainly.'

'I think we should display our wares before these
gentlemen commit themselves to a purchase,' said
Osbourne. 'I'm sure they'd like to see the girl.' He
said it so simply that the councillors were impressed
with his figure of speech. Only his father and his
friend knew its stinging lash.

'A sensible suggestion,' someone muttered, and old
Ledwaba's protest choked in his throat. He sullenly
nodded assent, and Osbourne went to fetch Ellen.
After a while, she appeared in the doorway. Her
father tried his last trick.

'There's no need to say anything, my child. The
gentlemen merely wish to see you.'

'But I have something to say, father, something drastic.' Her father sank slowly into a chair. She turned to the men. 'My fathers, I know the woman should be silent and suffer her elders and betters to determine her fate. Still, believe me, this way is best. You are here to make me a wife to Dikgang. What I think of him is entirely irrelevant. But you must know that I belong to another, not so much from wilfulness of my rebel heart, but because by the law of man and of God, I cannot go to any man, but the man I love, as a virgin.'

And she walked out.

There was uproar. Reggie gaped. Osbourne tittered. Old Ledwaba sat bowed and broken. He hardly heard the grey-headed old man begin to speak:

'My brothers, let us not chatter like apes. Let us rather retire to deliberate on how to convince the Chief that we do not encourage the marriage, and how to avert a crisis in the tribe. Ledwaba, we shall try to suppress the insult to the Royal House. We say no more, for we know how you suffer. Do you hear?'

He did not hear; he would not hear or tell anything anymore.

THE WILL TO DIE

I have heard much, have read much more, of the Will to Live; stories of fantastic retreats from the brink of death at moments when all hope was lost. To the aid of certain personalities in the bleakest crises, spiritual resources seem to come forward from what? Character? Spirit? Soul? Or the Great Reprieve of a Spiritual Clemency — hoisting them back from the muddy slough of the Valley of the Shadow.

But the Will to Die has intrigued me more . . .

I have also heard that certain snakes can hypnotize their victim, a rat, a frog or a rabbit, not only so that it cannot flee to safety in the overwhelming urge for survival, but so that it is even attracted towards its destroyer, and appears to enjoy dancing towards its doom. I have often wondered if there is not some mesmeric power that Fate employs to engage some men deliberately, with macabre relish, to seek their destruction and to plunge into it.

Take Foxy . . .

His real name was Philip Matauoane, but for some reason, I think from the excesses of his college days, everybody called him Foxy. He was a teacher in a

small school in Barberton, South Africa. He had been
to Fort Hare University College in the Cape Province,
and had majored in English (with distinction) and
Native Administration. Then he took the University
Education Diploma (teaching) with Rhodes University,
Grahamstown.

He used to say, 'I'm the living exemplar of the
modern, educated African's dilemma. I read English
and was trained to be a teacher — the standard
profession for my class these days; but you never
know which government department is going to expel
you and pitchfork you into which other government
department. So I also took Native Administration as a
safety device.'

You would think that that labels the cautious,
providential kind of human.

Foxy was a short fellow, the type that seems in
youth to rush forward towards old age, but somewhere, around the eve of middle-age, stops dead
and ages no further, almost forever. He had wide,
owlish eyes, and a trick with his mouth that suggested
withering contempt for all creation. He invariably
wore clothes that swallowed him: the coat over-
flowed and drowned his arms, the trousers sat on his
chest in front and billowed obscenely behind. He was
a runt of a man.

But in that unlikely body resided a live, restless
brain.

When Foxy first left college he went to teach
English at Barberton High School. He was twenty-five
then, and those were the days when high school
pupils were just ripe to provoke or prejudice a young
man of indifferent morals. He fell in love with a
young girl, Betty Kumalo, his own pupil.

I must explain this spurious phenomenon of

'falling in love'. Neither Foxy nor Betty had the remotest sense of commitment to the irrelevance of marrying some day. The society of the times was such that affairs of this nature occurred easily. Parents did not mind much. Often they would invite a young teacher to the home, and as soon as he arrived, would eclipse themselves, leaving the daughter with stern but unmistakable injunctions to 'be hospitable to the teacher'.

We tried to tell Foxy, we his fellow-teachers, that this arrangement was too nice to be safe, but these things had been written in the stars.

Foxy could not keep away from Betty's home. He could not be discreet. He went there every day, every unblessed day. He took her out during week-ends and they vanished into the countryside in his ancient Chevrolet.

On Mondays he would often say to me, 'I don't know what's wrong with me. I know this game is dangerous. I know Betty will destroy me, but that seems to give tang to the adventure. Hopeless. Hopeless.' And he would throw his arms out.

I had it out with him once.

'Foxy,' I said, 'you must stop this nonsense. It'll ruin you.'

There came a glint of pleasure, real ecstasy it seemed to me, into his eyes. It was as if the prospect of ruin was hallelujah.

He said to me, 'My intelligence tells me that it'll ruin me, but there's a magnetic force that draws me to that girl, and another part of me, much stronger than intelligence, simply exults.'

'Marry her then, and get done with it.'

'No!' He said it so vehemently that I was quite alarmed. 'Something in me wants that girl pregnant but not as my wife.'

I thought it was a hysterical utterance.

You cannot go flinging wild oats all over a fertile field, not even wild weeds. It had to happen.

If you are a school-teacher, you can only get out of a situation like that if you marry the girl, that is if you value your job. Foxy promptly married — another girl! But he was smart enough to give Betty's parents fifty pounds. That, in the hideous system of *lobola*, the system of bride-price, made Betty his second wife. And no authority on earth could accuse him of seduction.

But when his wife found out about it she battered him, as the Americans would say, 'To hell and back'.

Foxy started drinking heavily.

Then another thing began to happen; Foxy got drunk during working hours. Hitherto, he had been meticulous about not cultivating his iniquities in the teeth of his job, but now he seemed to be splashing in the gutter with a will.

I will never forget the morning another teacher and I found him stinking drunk about half an hour before school was to start. We forced him into a shebeen and asked the queen to let him sleep it off. We promised to make the appropriate excuses to the headmaster on his behalf. Imagine our consternation when he came reeling into the assembly hall where we were saying morning prayers with all the staff and pupils. How I prayed that morning!

These things happen. Everybody noticed Foxy's condition, except, for some reason, the headmaster. We hid him in the Biology Laboratory for the better part of the day, but that did not make the whole business any more edifying. Happily, he made his appearance before we could perjure ourselves to the headmaster. Later however, we learned that he had told the shebeen queen that he would go to school perforce because we were trying to get him into trouble for absence from work and that we wished to 'outshine' him. Were we livid!

Every one of his colleagues gave him a dressing down. We told him that no more was he alone in this: it involved the dignity of us all. The whole location was beginning to talk nastily about us. Moreover, there was a violent, alcoholic concoction brewed in the location called Barberton. People began to link 'Barberton', 'High' and 'School' to make puns about us.

Superficially it hurt him to cause us so much trouble, but something deep down in him did not allow him really to care. He went on drinking hard. His health was beginning to crack under it. Now he met every problem with the gurgling answer of the bottle.

One night I heard that he was very ill, so I went to see him at home. His wife had long since given him up for lost; they no longer shared a bedroom. I found him in his room. The scene was ghastly. He was lying in his underwear in bed linen which was stained with the blotches of murdered bugs. There was a plate of uneaten food that must have been there since the day before yesterday. He was breathing heavily. Now and then he tried to retch, but nothing came up. His bloodshot eyes rolled this way and that, and whenever some respite graciously came, he reached out for a bottle of gin and gulped at it until the fierce liquid poured over his stubbled chin.

He gibbered so that I thought he was going mad. Then he would retch violently again, that jolting, vomitless quake of a retch.

He needed a doctor but he would not have one. His wife carped, 'Leave the pig to perish.'

I went to fetch the doctor nevertheless. We took quite a while, and when we returned his wife sneered at us, 'You wouldn't like to see him now.' We went into his room and found him lost in oblivion. A strange girl was lying by his side.

In his own house!

I did not see him for weeks, but I had heard enough. They said that he was frequenting dangerous haunts. One drunken night he was beaten up and robbed. Another night he returned home stark naked, without a clue as to who had stripped him.

Liquor should have killed him, but some compulsive urge chose differently. After a binge one night, he wandered hopelessly about the dark location streets, seeking his home. At last, he decided on a gate, a house, a door. He was sure that that was his home. He banged his way in, ignored the four or five men singing hymns in the sitting-room, and staggered into the bedroom. He flung himself on to the bed and hollered, 'Woman, it's time that I sleep in your bed. I'm sick and tired of being a widower with a living wife.'

The men took up sticks and battered Foxy to a pulp. They got it into their heads that the woman of the house had been in the business all the time; that only now had her lover gone and got drunk enough to let the cat out of the bag. They beat the woman too, within millimetres of her life. All of them landed in jail for long stretches.

But I keep having a stupid feeling that somehow, Philip 'Foxy' Matauoane would have felt: 'This is as it should be.'

Some folks live the obsession of death.

THE NICE TIME GIRL

'Damn it all, I'm going to the party,' Eunice Maoela finally said to herself, putting aside the crudely-printed party ticket that Maggie Modise had given her in Prinsloo Street, Pretoria. She went into the bathroom to wash up, all the time worrying about her cruel lot. Theophilus Maoela, her forty-four-year-old husband, was 'too cold' for her, and in any case he was away most of the time at a teaching post in far-away Phokeng, outside Rustenburg, coming home rarely for weekends. And then her only son was staying with her mother in Pietersburg. She strode into her bedroom.

'Damn it all, I'm going!'

So she put on a sheath costume with a provocative slit along one leg, and went to the party in Tladi Street, Atteridgeville. Right from the gate she flung herself into the party. She swayed her hips and slid her feet to the rhythms of the jive-number. A Johannesburg jive sheik rudely left his partner and made for her.

'Baby, he said, 'what you got don't matter; it's what you give — now, c'mon give, give, give!' snapping

his fingers at each 'give' and swaying his knees slowly.
She broke into her own ad lib, a complicated inter-
twining of her legs that moved like the spokes of
a spinning wheel. How did she manage it in that
sheath costume? Maybe that's how that costume got
its slit.

When the number ended the crowd that had
stopped to watch them cheered. Eunice felt that she
was once more in those reckless days before marriage.
Her partner led her into the house and ordered two
beers. They found a corner on a studio couch and
talked, whilst some Lady Selbourne boys crooned.

'I'm Matthew Modise, from George Goch,' he said
'Related to the Modises here. I came over with some
Rand boys.' He paused, waiting for her to introduce
herself. But she was scared, now that the first wild
fling was over. After all, Johannesburg boys are
dangerous! So he went on. 'I didn't know Pretoria
dames could jive like that. Baby, you're hot stuff!'
His praise warmed her to him. The beer came endless-
ly, to help break down her resistance. Now and then
they went to the veranda to jive, and when they did
so, the veranda was all theirs.

'Honey,' he said at length, 'let's blow to some cosy
spot. This crowd just ain't private.'

'Come to my joint,' she said impulsively. She knew
he was a playboy, but she wanted to play a dangerous
game.

'Sure it's safe?' he asked uneasily.

'Sure!'

At her home in Seiso Street she gave him a meal.
That night Eunice told Matthew the story of her
wretched marriage, of her husband's coldness and her
loneliness.

'Look, Eunice,' Matthew said, 'how about chancing it with me?' She was silent for a long time, so he argued feverishly — 'you don't see the blues'll get you. Maybe not now, maybe not tomorrow, but they'll get you right enough. An' then you'll grab any worm that comes along. It ain't gonna be me, it ain't gonna be no guy you go for, cos you're just gonna be goddam desperate. Me too, I'm gonna go to pieces, thinkin' of you, an' maybe just snatch any tart that comes my way. An' two lives'll be busted.'

'If only he'd do a wicked thing,' she sobbed. 'If only I could catch him drunk or with another woman . . . but you don't walk out on a man just like that . . . . Moreover, Matthew, there's my boy — '

'I don't mind, darling,' he misunderstood her. 'I gotta boy myself.'

'Mm-mm, that's not the point,' she replied. 'I'm afraid if my husband can prove that I'm unfit to raise the kid, I'll lose it.'

The following morning when he left, Matthew said, 'Here's my address in case you want me.'

She looked him straight in the face, and said, 'My boy means more to me than nice times.'

But for the whole of the following week Eunice felt that she had missed a lifetime's opportunity to escape. She felt defeated. To make matters worse Theophilus came home that week-end. The contrast between this tame, genial husband and her vivacious jive-king stood out roughly. She knew one taste made her hunger for more of the forbidden fruit of the other night.

On the Monday after Theophilus had left, she went to George Goch, and only after painting the city red for three days did she return to Atteridgeville.

Three weeks later Theophilus Maoela was quietly reading in his sitting-room. He had arrived the evening before.

It was a Saturday morning, and his wife had just returned from the Post Office to send a wire to somebody or other. Now she was busy in the kitchen preparing the midday meal. The thought crossed his mind that his wife might be lonely, what with his long periods away from home, and the fact that he was too tired or too busy to give her a good time. He thought it over for a long time. Then at table he spoke.

'My dear,' he said, 'couldn't we visit your ma in Lady Selbourne some time this afternoon? It's so lonely here.'

What a lame attempt to cheer up this bleak life, she thought. But aloud she said, 'I want to be with you, dear . . . alone with you. Tell you what, let's take a long walk this evening. Perhaps we'll rediscover the old magic of our love.' So sweetly was this said that the husband sighed, 'Ah — ' But before their evening walk Eunice had to go out again.

Husband and wife walked out of the location into the veld beyond the main road. Out of sight they held hands, and chewed stalks, and didn't even think of snakes in the grass. Suddenly, out of the tall grass leapt four or five evil-looking men. Eunice screamed but the shock must have been too sudden for her voice to carry. Theophilus sprang to her defence, and when the attackers struck he fought with bare hands. But the odds were too great for him, and he was clubbed unconscious. Then the butchers stabbed him to death in cold, greasy blood. After that, gloved hands went through his pockets, turned them inside out, but found only small-change. The motive looked like robbery! A few minutes later a car roared away.

'But, why didn't you run for help, Mrs Maoela? We could've cordoned off the car in a few minutes.'

'When they struck him down, I fainted.'

'Yes I see that. Can you describe any of the attackers?'

'It was dim . . . darkening twilight . . . and I fainted too soon . . . . '

Detective Mphahlele bit his nails, frowning pensively. The trouble is that the hoodlums acted too swiftly. Then that car. The mark it left on the hard road had been blurred by other car tracks. Then the spot. The motive was obviously robbery. But who was so stupid as to lie in tall grass to rob people at a place where people rarely passed. Where the only activity was motorists flying past at breakneck speed? The detective cursed all unmethodical criminals.

Then he tried the angle of Mrs Maoela's answers. Barren answers! They were such a dead-end that he chose to think of the pretty Mrs Maoela herself. Yes, lovely woman that! But she looked lonely. Anyway, who wouldn't look down when his spouse had just been brutally murdered? Ah, yes! the murder . . . . That's the job. Must get back to the answers . . . .

He racked his brain for a solution until sheer fatigue made him numb in the head, and he found he wasn't thinking anymore. Just spinning round and round in a dizzy nightmare. He decided to sleep on it. And the following day he would study the reports of the other men on the case.

'I'll try to let you know now and then, Mrs Maoela, how things are shaping,' he said as he rose to go out. But from the way he walked, it seemed clear that he didn't expect things to take any sensible shape at all.

'Philip! Philip! Wake up, wake up!' Mrs Mphahlele
shook her husband, huddled up beneath the warm
blankets.

It was a matter of emergency. He stirred and
groaned. Then one eye popped open. 'Philip, Constable
Mushi is here to see you. He says it's urgent, and he
must talk to you personally.' Detective Mphahlele
crept out of the warm nest and, still in his pyjamas,
stumbled out to see the constable.

'Yes, Darkie, what's up?' He yawned.

Constable Mushi spoke carefully.

'Five fellows from Jo'burg were caught with a
stolen car last night. They had no stolen goods with
them, no liquor, no dagga, no nothing. But a big,
blood-stained butcher knife was found in the car.
Commandant Joubert wants you to come to the
police station immediately.'

'I see,' said the now fully awake Detective Mphahlele. 'Well let me get ready to go.'

Eunice received Detective Mphahlele with dumbfounded panic.

'Do not be afraid, Mrs Maoela. I've only come to
fulfil a promise. I told you that I'd let you know how
things are shaping.'

Her throat felt dry and sour. Detective Mphahlele
spoke slowly and clearly.

'My dear Mrs Maoela, it's really terrible how these
Johannesburg criminals think that Pretoria is a push-
over. It hurts my pride. Some day we've got to teach
them a thorough lesson . . . . '

Eunice found the suspense excruciating. 'Mphahlele!
Do you not realise that my husband's dead; that I'm
not interested in a policeman's pride. I expect you to

arrest the murderers!'

He sighed. 'Yes, Mrs Maoela, I've got to get the murderers — *all* of them. Let me tell you how far we've got. Last night, a speed cop stopped a Johannesburg car on the Pretoria-Johannesburg road for speeding and reckless driving. He found that it was a car stolen three days ago in Johannesburg. The fellows in the car tried something funny, but the speed cop had a colleague close by. They were brought back to Pretoria. Mrs Maoela, in that car we found a heavy bloodstained butcher knife. It didn't take much questioning to get the truth out of them. We have methods, Mrs Maoela, very persuasive methods.

'Now, four of those fellows are hardened criminals, well-known at Marshall Square — you know that's the main Johannesburg police station. They have also spent long stretches in the Fort, Johannesburg's jail. But one fellow hasn't a record at all. Of course, there hasn't been much time to check up as yet. But the others said that it was he who bought them for the killing. Strangely enough, he claims that a woman bought *him*. Well, we know cornered rats will always try to shift the blame onto others. We wanted proof. He said proof could be found in a telegram this woman sent him making the appointment for the murder of your husband. The police in Johannesburg are searching his room in George Goch for the telegram. We also want to find out if it is true that many people in George Goch can testify that he and this woman were friends . . . intimate friends, Mrs Maoela.'

Eunice couldn't take any more. 'Yes, I did it! I did it! Life with my husband had become intolerable!'

she shouted hysterically.

That night Detective Mphahlele asked his wife, 'I wonder why Beauty sometimes becomes the Beast?'

TEN-TO-TEN

The curfew proper for all Africans in Marabastad, Pretoria, was 10 pm. By that hour every African; man, woman, and child, had to be indoors, preferably in bed; if the police caught you abroad without a 'special permit' you were hauled off to the battleship-grey little police station in First Avenue, near the Aapies River, and clapped in jail. The following morning you found yourself trembling before a magistrate in one of those out-rooms that served as a court, and after a scathing lecture, you were fined ten bob. So it behoved everyone, every black mother's son, to heed that bell and be off the streets at ten.

But it was strange how the first warning bell at ten-to-ten exercised a power of panic among us, really out of all proportion. I suppose, watchless at night, when that bell went off and you were still streets away from your house, you did not know whether it was the first warning — ten-to-ten — giving you that much grace to hurry you on, or the fatal ten o' clock bell itself.

However, there were ever women in their yards, peering over corrugated-iron fences and bedstead gates, calling in sing-song voices, 'Ten-to-ten! Ten-to-ten!' as if the sound of the bell at the police station down there in First Avenue was itself echoed, street after street, urging the belated on, homewards, bed-wards, safe from the Law.

As the first bell rang, one Saturday night, a huge African policeman roused himself from the barracks. He was enormous. Nearer seven feet than six feet tall, he towered over his fellow men like a sheer mountain above the mites in the valley. Perfectly formed, his shoulders were like boulders, his arms like the trunks of elephants, the muscles hard and corded. His legs bore his magnificent torso like sturdy pillars under some granite superstructure. He had the largest foot in Pretoria, size fifteen, and people used to say, 'His boot is special made from the factory'. He was coal-black, with the shiny blackness of ebony, but had large, rolling, white eyes and thick, bluish lips.

He gave a last, critical scrutiny to his shining, black boots and black uniform with tinny buttons, before he stepped into the charge office to report for duty. His was the night-beat. Every night at ten o'clock he went out with one or two other policemen to roam the dusty streets of Marabastad Location and clear them of vagrants. People looked at him with awe; nobody ever argued with him; when his immense shadow fell across you, you shrivelled, or, if you had any locomotion left in you, you gave way fast.

They called him Ten-to-Ten because of that night beat of his, and he was known by no other name. Ten-to-Ten's strength was prodigious and there were many legends in the location about him . . . .

There was the one that he originally came from Tzaneen in the Northern Transvaal to seek work in Pretoria. One day he was sitting in a drinking house

when a young location hooligan came in and molested
the daughter of the house. The girl's father tried to
protest but the young hooligan slapped him across
the face and told him to shut up. Ten-to-Ten was not
accustomed to such behaviour, so he rose from the
corner where he was sitting with his tin of beer and
walked up to the young man.

'Look,' he said, 'you can't go on like this in
another man's house. Please go away now.' He gently
pushed the young man towards the door. 'Come on,
now, go home.'

The young man swung round with a curse,
hesitated a moment when he saw the great bulk of
the man confronting him, then with a sneer drew a
knife.

They say you can pester a Venda from the North,
that you can insult him, humiliate him in public
or cheat him in private, but there are two things you
just cannot do with impunity: take his girl, or draw a
knife on him.

That night, Ten-to-Ten went jungle-mad.

'Ha!' he snarled.

The knife flashed and caught him in the forearm,
spurting blood. But before the young man could
withdraw it, Ten-to-Ten had caught him by the neck
and dragged him out of the house. In the yard there
was the usual corrugated-iron fence. Swinging the boy
like wet laundry, Ten-to-Ten lashed him against the
fence repeatedly until the fence broke down. Then he
started strangling him. Men came running from their
houses. They tried to tear Ten-to-Ten off the boy,
but he shook them off like flakes. Soon, somebody
sounded a whistle, the call for the police. By the time
they came Ten-to-Ten was hurling all sorts of back-
yard missiles at the small crowd that sought to

protect the boy.

The police stormed him and knocked him over, bludgeoning him with batons. They managed to manacle his wrists while he was down on his back, then they stepped back to wipe their sweat and wait for him to rise. Ten-to-Ten rose slowly on one knee. He looked at the police and smiled. The white sergeant was saying, 'Now, now, come quietly, no more trouble, eh?' when Ten-to-Ten spotted his enemy staggering from the crowd.

He grunted savagely and, looking at his bound hands, wrenched them apart and snapped the iron manacles like cotton. The police had to rush at him again while the crowd scattered.

They say the desk sergeant at the police station decided that very day to make Ten-to-Ten a policeman, and Marabastad became a peaceful location.

That is the kind of story you do not have to believe to enjoy.

Another time, legend has it, the coal-delivery man had some difficulty with his horse. He had a one-man horse-cart with which he delivered coal from door to door. On one occasion, the horse suddenly shied, perhaps having been pelted by mischievous boys with slings, and went dashing down the narrow avenue, scattering women with water tins on their heads. Just then Ten-to-Ten came round the corner. He caught the bridle of the horse and struggled to keep it still, being carried along a few yards himself. The horse reared and threatened to break away. Then Ten-to-Ten kicked it with his size fifteen boot under the heart. The horse sagged, rolled over and died.

But it was not only for his violent exploits that we thrilled to him. Ten-to-Ten played soccer for the Police First Eleven. He played right-back. For a giant his size he was remarkably swift, but it was his antics we loved. He would drop an oncoming ball dead before his own goal-posts, and as the opponent's poor forward came rushing at him, he would quickly shift aside with the ball at the last moment, leaving the forward to go hurtling on his own momentum through the goal-posts. Derisively, he would call, 'Goal!' and the excited spectators would shout, 'Ten-to-Ten! Ten-to-Ten!'

Sometimes he would approach the ball ferociously, with his rivals all about it, and he would make as if he was going to blast them ball and all. They would scuttle for cover, only to find that he had stopped the ball and was standing with one foot on it, grinning happily.

When he *did* elect to kick it, he had such powerful shots that the ball went from one end of the field to the other. Once, they say, he took a penalty kick. The ball went with such force that when the goalie tried to stop it, his hands were flayed and the deflected ball still went on to tear a string in the net.

'Ten-to-Ten!'

Yes, he had a sense of humour; and he was also the understanding kind. He knew about his great strength and seldom exercised it recklessly.

In the Marabastad of those days there was a very quarrelsome little fellow called Shorty. He was about four-feet six, but as they say, 'He buys a tickey's beer and makes a pound's worth of trouble.' No-one but Shorty ever really took his tantrums seriously, but people enjoyed teasing him for fun.

'Shorty,' they once told him, 'Ten-to-Ten's in that house telling people that you're not a man, but just a sample.' Shorty boiled over. He strutted into the house with the comic little gait of the very short and found Ten-to-Ten sitting with a tin of beer in his hands.

He kicked the tin of beer out of Ten-to-Ten's hands, nearly toppling himself over in the process, and shouted, 'A sample of a man, eh? I'll teach you to respect your betters. Come outside and fight.' The others quickly signalled Ten-to-Ten that it was all a joke and he caught on. But Shorty was so aggrieved that he pestered Ten-to-Ten all afternoon.

At last Ten-to-Ten, tired of the sport, rose, lifted Shorty bodily off the ground and carried him down the street with a procession of cheering people behind them. Shorty was raging; he threw futile punches at Ten-to-Ten's chest. His dangling legs were kicking about furiously, but Ten-to-Ten carried him all the way to the police station.

It was a startled desk sergeant who suddenly found a midget landed on his desk, shouting, 'I'll kill him! I'll kill him!'

'What's this?' the sergeant wanted to know.

Wearily, Ten-to-Ten explained, 'He says he wants to give me a fair fight.'

Shorty was fined ten bob, and when he came out of there, he turned to Ten-to-Ten disgustedly, and spat, 'Coward!'

Ten-to-Ten walked with two other policemen, Constables Masemola and Ramokgopa, up First Avenue into glittering Boom Street. It was like suddenly walking out of an African slum into a chunk of the Orient. They strolled slowly up the tarred Boom Street, past the Empire Cinema. Now and then they would stop to look at the exotic foods in the window of some Indian shop, and the pungent smells of Eastern cooking and Eastern toiletry would rise to their nostrils. A hundred yards ahead, you could see the Africans who had no special permits to be out at night, sorting themselves from the Indian and coloured night crowds and dodging down some dark streets. They had long noticed the stalwart shadow of Ten-to-Ten coming up. He knew it too, but did not bother.

He reasoned that as long as they were scampering home, it was a form of respect for the Law. Unlike some of the other policemen who ferreted out Africans and delighted in chasing them down the road, even when he caught one or two on the streets at night, it was enough for him to say, 'You there, home!' As they fled before him he felt duty to have been done.

Then they turned into the dark of Second Avenue of the location, away from where their eyes were guided by the blinking neons, into the murky streets where only their feet found the familiar way. It was silent, but Ten-to-Ten knew the residents were around, the silence was only because he was there. He was walking down the street, a presence that suddenly hushed these normally noisy people. In fact, he had heard their women, as he entered the street, calling down along it, 'Ten-to-Ten! Ten-to-Ten!'

It was not like the adulatory cheering on the soccer field, this calling of 'Ten-to-Ten!' This one had a long, dreary, plaintive note . . . to carry it far along the street? or to express heartfelt agony? In the field he felt their pride in him, the admiration for his wonderful physique, his skill and his sense of humour. The rapport between himself and his spectators who lined the field was delicious. There even the puniest of them would rush into the field after he had scored a goal, slap him on the back happily, and say, 'Ai, but you, you Ten-to-Ten.'

He would come off the field and find a hero-worshipping youngster carrying his coat and pants to him, and another pushing his glittering Hercules bicycle. A small boy would push out his robin chest and yell, 'Ten-to-Ten!' unselfconsciously.

But here, people skulked behind tin shacks and wailed their misery at whatever perverse god crushed them round about the hour of ten. Some of them were probably muttering in whispers even now as he passed. Had he not seen lower down the street a light suddenly go out in a house? It was probably a drinking house where they sat in the dark with their calabashes and tins trying to find their 'blind mouths', with the auntie of the house hissing importunately, 'Simeon shut up, you fool, don't you know it's Ten-to-Ten?'

They passed a church and fancied they heard a rustling sound on the porch. They went to investigate. Out and past them bolted a boy and a girl. Ten-to-Ten mocked his shock after them, 'What, even in the House of the Lord!' They ran faster.

Fifth Street was empty and dark, but before long they heard familiar grunting sounds. Ten-to-Ten signalled the other policemen to walk quietly. Off the street, hidden in an opening among tall grass, was a group of dice players. They had formed a ring, inside which a candle was shielded from the breezes. The thrower would retreat a little from the ring and, shaking his dice in his bowled fist, lunge forward, and cast them into the patch of light, giving a visceral grunt to coax his luck. Coins of the stake lay in the centre.

Creeping low, Ten-to-Ten and his mates tip-toed up to them. They were so intent on the game that they heard nothing until suddenly he rose to his great height, like Mephistopheles out of the gloom, and bellowed, 'Ten-to-Ten!'

They splashed in all directions. One boy jumped into Ten-to-Ten and bounced back, falling to the ground. A policeman put a boot on his shoulder with just enough pressure to keep him there. Another chap never even got up, a rough hand had caught him by the neck. The boy who had nursed the candle tried to get away faster than his body would allow him and his feet kept slipping under him in his haste like a panicking dog's on a hard smooth floor. He whimpered pointlessly, 'It's not me! It's not me!'

Ten-to-Ten roared with Olympian laughter, 'Haw! Haw! Haw!'

When the boy finally took ground, he catapulted away. The other policemen brought the two detainees up to Ten-to-Ten; he did not trouble to question them, just re-lighted the candle and held it in their frightened faces.

Then he said, 'Search them, Masemola. You know I'm only interested in knives.'

Constable Masemola searched them but found no knives. In the pocket of one he found a little tin containing a condom. He held it up to Ten-to-Ten like the finger of a glove. 'Sies!' said Ten-to-Ten disgustedly, brushing aside Masemola's hand. Then to the boys, 'Off with you!' and they crashed through the tall grass into the location.

The other constable had picked up the coins from the ground, and while Masemola was still wondering aloud what those boys thought they knew about the use of condoms, Ten-to-Ten noticed the other constable pocketing the coins. Again he just said, 'Sies!'

They went up Third Avenue, Ten-to-Ten thinking, thoughts for which he could find no words . . . .

Am I, perhaps, the only fool in this job? All the

other policemen take bribes, intimidate shopkeepers,
force half guilt-conscious women to go to bed with
them. Some beat up people needlessly, a few actually
seem to enjoy the wanton slap, the unprovoked blow,
the unreturnable kick for their own selves. Of course,
it's seldom necessary for me to hit anybody. Before
my bulk the runts fly. Maybe that's why. Maybe if I
were little like these chaps I'd also want to push
people around.

But, really, you should hear these policemen
grumble when the white sergeant barks at them in the
charge office. Then they know they're black; that the
whiteman is unreasonable, unjust, bossy, a bastard.
But, God! See these chaps in the location on the beat.
They treat their own people like ordure. And when
the whiteman is with us on the beat, they surpass
themselves. Damn that Ramokgopa! I felt so ashamed
the other day when he hit a hopeless drunk with a
baton until Sergeant du Toit had to say, 'That's
enough now, Ramokgopa.' God, I felt ashamed! The
blackman strikes, the whiteman says, 'That's enough,
now.'

And this business of making women sleep with
you because you caught them with a drum of illicit
beer. I can't understand it. If I want a piece of
bottom and, by God, now and then the fierce,
burning pang stabs me too — then I want the woman
to want me too, to come alive under me, not to lie
there like a dead fish. The thing's rape, man, however
much she consented.

What do I want in this job, anyway. It's a bastard
of a job. Funny hours, low pay, strange orders that
make no sense, violence, ever violence, and the daily
spectacle of the degradation of my people. Well, I
suppose it's a job. Otherwise I'd be with those work-

less fellows we corner every day and arrest for not having passes. Hell, if I hadn't taken this job, I'm sure I'd be in jail now. Jail? God, me, I'd long ago have been hanged for murder if some policeman handled me as our chaps manhandle these poor devils.

But I have to work. I came here to work because I like to work. No, because back home in Tzaneen the people are starving, the rains haven't come these many years and the land is crying out, giving up the vain struggle to live — to push up one little green blade, to justify herself — she just lies there like a barren, passionless woman, seeing men hunger and die. No, but really because Mapula is waiting for me. Mapula? Ahhh! The memory stings me and I feel the subtle, nameless pain that only a big man knows, I can't cry . . . I can't cry . . . .

They came out of the location, again into Boom Street whose bright lights seemed to crackle into his twilight consciousness. They came out at the bicycle shop.

A bicycle shop, by nature, repaired bicycles and sold spare parts, and there was always an upturned bicycle, one or other wheel missing, supposedly in the process of repair, outside the shop or at night in the window. But in Marabastad it was more of a music shop where the most raucous, the screechiest, the bawdiest cacophonies of township jazz bawled and caterwauled from the 78s inside to loudspeakers outside. 'WeSelina, go greet me your ma!' shrieked the lonesome son-in-law loud enough for his sweetheart, Selina, or indeed the mother-in-law herself, to hear him back in the Reserves.

Ten-to-Ten looked at his pocket-watch. Twenty-to-twelve. Odd, he thought, here was a coloured girl dancing to music that was distinctly African township jazz — this chance thought was soon dispersed by the sight of the crowds that spilled from the Empire Cinema. Most of them were well-dressed Indian men with lovely coloured girls; there were few Indian girls. A sprinkling of African men was in the crowd, but from their unalarmed expressions one could easily see that they had been to school and had the 'papers'.

As they strolled along the pavement the policemen saw an old Zulu, clad in a greenish-khaki military over-coat, huddling over a glowing brazier. He was the *matshingilane* — the nightwatchman. It was not clear which building he was guarding; probably several Indian bosses had chipped in to get him to look after the whole row of buildings. Lucky devil! Most times he slept well, safe in the knowledge that a policeman on the beat would stroll up and down watching the buildings for him.

'*Poisa! Poisa!* — Police! Police! They're killing an African man down there!'

Ten-to-Ten and his mates dashed down the street. They found a crowd of Indians pummelling a young African man. Ten-to-Ten barged into them like a bull-dozer, pushing the crowd this way and that, until he got to the man on the ground.

'What's going on here?' he barked.

Scores of voices replied, 'He's a thief!'

'A pickpocket!'

'The lady's handbag!'

'He hit the gentleman first!'

'He bumped him!'

'And swore at him!'

'He's always robbing people!'

'We know him! We know him!'

Ten-to-Ten lifted the African from the ground. The

man cowered before the enormous form over him.

'Well?' Ten-to-Ten asked.

'They lie,' was all the man could say for himself.

Somebody tried to grab at the man but Ten-to-Ten pushed him away and pulled the victim towards himself, more protectively, saying, 'No, you don't.'

Then he addressed the crowd. 'Look here, I'm going to arrest this man and no-one is going to take him away from me. No-one, you hear?' He was quiet for a moment and looked around challengingly. Then he continued. 'Now is there anybody who cares to lay a charge against him?'

There were murmurings, but no definite charge. Someone called out, weakly, 'But he's a thief.'

Ten-to-Ten said, 'All right, come forward and lay a charge.'

Instead, a hand again reached for the man. Ten-to-Ten released his charge for a moment to go after the owner of the hand, a half-impulsive movement.

'Look out!' someone yelled, and the crowd surged away. Ten-to-Ten spun round and saw that the African had drawn a long knife.

'Awright, come for me, you bastards!' he growled.

The savage blood leapt inside Ten-to-Ten. He lunged at the man like a black flash. If the knife had been shorter, he would have got it in the neck, but it was unwieldy and only slashed him across the shoulder.

'Ah!' soughed the fascinated crowd.

Ten-to-Ten caught the man's knife-arm at the wrist and above the elbow, then brought it down on his upthrust knee. Crack! It snapped like a dry twig.

The sharp shriek curdled the night air and the knife went clattering to the pavement. The man went down to the ground whining, and the fury passed out of

Ten-to-Ten.

Quietly, he said to the man, 'I could have killed you for that . . . knife.'

The crowd broke up into the night in little groups.

Ten-to-Ten said to Masemola, with a careless wave of the hand, 'Take him to De la Rey. I'm coming.'

He stood thinking, This was my bad night, the young, bloody fool!

MARTA

The people in the queue stood drearily with an air of defeat waiting over them. Sophiatown on Monday mornings is like that. An anti-climax after Sunday's excesses.

Then Marta came along, still drunk. Her baby was hanging dangerously on her back as she staggered up Victoria Road. Somebody in the queue remarked drily, 'S'funny how a drunk woman's child never falls.'

'Shet-up!' said Marta in the one vulgar word she knew.

She stood, swaying a moment on her heels, and watched the people in the queue bitterly. A bus swung round the Gibson Street corner and narrowly missed hitting her. Three or four women in the queue screamed, 'Oooo!' But Marta just turned and staggered off into Gibson Street, the child carelessly hanging on her back.

There was no gate to the yard in Gibson Street, because there was no fence to make a gate into. So Marta just walked up to the house. She toed the door open, and just then, feeling that she was going to be

sick, dived for the unmade bed. The child nearly shot
out of the pocket on Marta's back. It started crying,
but Marta just said, 'Shet-up.'

A tall African whose complexion was five minutes
to midnight turned round from the mirror, his hands
arrested around a half-made tie-knot. He had a shock
of hair on his head which made him look like a tall
golliwog.

In his eyes an anger crept like the back-splash of
the tide. His upper lip curled, showing a flash of the
whitest teeth. When he spoke it was in a sort of a
snarl.

'S'true's God, Marta,' he growled with that abrupt
accent of the Rhodesian, 'one of these days I go to
chock you tille you die. I'll teash you to stop drinking
and for to start looking after your house — ' And just
as if to make his point, he stepped into a plate with
dry morsels of food that crunched under his weight.
'Agh, sies!' he hissed.

'Aw, shet-up, man!'

For a moment he stood there and stared at her
in stark, stupid fury. Then suddenly he was galvanized
into action. He leapt at her and grabbed her by the
throat, squeezing, squeezing . . . .

What's the use of fretting? Life is too large for
that. And life must be lived — sweetly or bitterly —
but always intensely. It is like a burning log that
crackles at every knot and explodes in little bursting
pellets of fire. The pain or the slow-creeping sorrow.
The sudden fear of dark location alleys. The shifting
aside to avoid the attention of young hooligans who
sit and swear on the street corners. Then the wild, fire-
mad midnight parties. Getting drunk. It comes on
you in fumes, thick folds of smoke that trap you and
cloud you. And suddenly, illogically, the police! The

police! The police! What's the use? You carry a
dangerous weapon, the police get you. You go
without one, the tsotsis get you. But it is nice to have
a woman, your woman, made yours by the long
moment of fierce love and the close embrace, tighter,
tighter, tighter . . . .

Until a child cries in sudden panic!

Jackson realised with a shock what he was doing.
Had he killed Marta? O God! What had he done? He
saw all the tawdry, vulgar, violent recklessness of
their lives. Something just keeps coming off wrong in
this hit and run mislife. And it's not so much Marta's
drinking or his adulteries . . . . It's — it's — it's, well,
dammitall!

Marta stirred and coughed. She tried to rise but found
that she could not. Hoarsely she said to Jackson,
'The child, the child.' He saw where she had pinned
him down with her body. He lifted her and pulled out
the child. Then he stood there looking at Marta and
the child anxiously. He felt they needed care . . . but
then a man's got to go to work.

You do anything, but you go to work. The police
arrest you by mistake; you do your all to get out,
because you got to go to work. You pay Admission
of Guilt. You admit anything, anything! So long as
you go to work. But sometimes you got to go to
jail. Then you go. It does not matter. Almost everybody you know has been to jail.

But then that long queue of men you had seen at
your place of work, looking for work . . . .

Outside in the street, Jackson saw two little girls
suddenly breaking into a dance. For the sheer swing
of it! He thought of how well Marta could do it.

Marta lay quietly for some time. Her throat was

smarting, but her head was whirling less dizzily now.
Then she reached out for the child and dragged it
across her body. It felt like trying to hoist oneself
by tugging at your socks. But she made it in the end.

She examined the child carefully. It looked all
right. It was gurgling now. She put it down on the
bed again. Sleep came jaggedly.

She woke up to what sounded like wild yelling.
Then she saw them, shouting at her to come on and
get up. Sophia was there, Emily and Boet Mike. They
were nice. But Marta's head was still clanging. Drink
does that to you when it rushes out.

'Come-ahn,' said Emily 'Boet Mike's ship is in and
Sophia stands all right. He-e-e, Boet Mike say, a
bottle of straight! Sophia says, straight! Boet Mike
says, straight. We said, no, let's get Marta first!
Come-ahn, Marta!'

Marta hesitates. 'Jackson will kill me.'

Sophia looked as if she had never heard anything
quite so funny. 'Since when have you been scared of
Jackson?'

'All right,' Marta yielded, 'but let me first find
Pulani to look after the child.'

Sophia insisted that they go to her favourite
shebeen in Gerty Street, because her husband who
had got the 'shakes' does not go there. Not ever. Of
course, Marta did not like the woman of the house
in Gerty Street. She puts on such airs since she's got
her new radiogram. But it's not every day that Boet
Mike's ship is in and that Sophia stands right.

The house in Gerty Street was made up of a veranda,
then a room, then another room, then a back-veranda.
The first room was a combined sitting-room and
bedroom. The second one a combined dining-room

and kitchen. They went into the sitting-room bedroom.

Somebody in the dining-room kitchen was practising jazz solos on a set of drums. But Marta and company did not mind.

Boet Mike said, 'Straight.' And they brought a bottle of brandy that looked like guilty blood. They drank from the bottle first, slowly, Emily serving in to all sorts of glasses. She managed to serve an equal shot each time, because she measured the drink by her fingers into one glass which she in turn poured into all the others.

And the drum was raving on relentlessly. It was as if the drummer himself was getting drunk ahead of them.

The bottle went down slowly, but before it reached its ankles, Sophia who stood right said, 'Straight!'

Suddenly Marta sprang up and jived to the rhythms of the rumbling drums. The others chanted out for her. Marta's arms went out before her, her legs spread, her knees sagged, her eyes drooped, her mouth opened a little, and she moved forward in a shuffle like a creature drawn irresistibly, half-consciously, to its doom. She shuffled towards the dining-room kitchen.

The others followed her. In the other room the furniture had been moved aside and in one corner a young man surely not eighteen yet was beating the drums as though he wanted to work something evil out of him.

He suddenly broke into a rapid roll of raw rhythm. His arms were flailing in and out, so fast that they blurred. Marta was caught in the wild burst like a loose fish and chips wrapping churned up in a sudden gust of wind. She leapt up, and when she landed again her feet sprinkled about in an intricate tracery. Then

just as suddenly her feet stopped, so suddenly that
the shock still shivered through the rest of her body.
Infinitely minute tremblings.

The drummer was watching her now. Their
positions were reversed. It was she who was giving
him direction now. She was transmitting the wild
energy, with clenched teeth and open hands, creeping
towards him. Her every sudden movement tore a roar
from the drums.

Then abruptly she stopped, and the cymbals
clanged!

Marta sank tiredly into a chair. She felt that she had
come back from somewhere, had committed something before which her spirit had often quailed. She
didn't want to dance again, or drink any more She
looked at the boy behind the drums. He seemed very
shy, very young. Could he, could he really be that
innocent even after this thing he and she had done
together?

He rose and started to go out, but Sophia, quite
drunk now, would have none of it.

'Uh-uh, man, brother,' she drawled. 'Don't go yet.
Come with us, man. We stand right.'

He hesitated, looked at Marta shyly. She looked at
Sophia. She knew Sophia wanted him for herself, but
then she knew Sophia and didn't like it. Somehow
she felt this boy should not be dragged into their
company. There was something about him that, she
felt with stupid stubbornness, should be left intact.

'Come here, man, brother, come to Sophia.'

'No!' Marta was surprised at the violence of her
own voice.

Sophia giggled. 'So, you want him. Well, I don't
carre damn. You're a friend of mine, see?'

Marta caught the boy by the sleeve of his floral shirt. 'Let's get away from here! Quick!' The urgency in her voice impelled him.

Boet Mike said how about finishing off another straight, but she didn't wait to reply.

Outside Marta realised that she was drunker than she had thought. She looked up into the young man's face and tried to smile. 'Looks like you've got to take me home,' she said.

He gave her a look of sheerest adoration. It stung her to the softest centre. 'Look here, kid, I want you to promise me one thing. Promise me that you will never drink.'

'But I don't drink,' he protested.

'Still promise me that you will never drink.'

A flash of anger showed in his face. 'You think I'm a kid, eh?'

'Nnnnnnooooo,' she said thoughtfully. 'I don't mean just drinking. I mean don't go rough.'

He was shy again. So she said: 'O.K. Take me home. I'll try to explain there.'

'Honestly, Sophia, I didn't think that the explanation would take that long . . . all day. I didn't know that we were at my place so long. All I know is that Jackson just suddenly returned home. It was hopeless . . . I could see from his eyes that he thought I was revenging for what had happened that morning. But I couldn't do it! I couldn't do it with that boy!

'Maybe it's true I was fed-up with Jackson. Maybe I did want in my heart to make Jackson feel that other men could like me. But not with that boy, Sophia. Not with that boy.

'Now the people say, "No case at all". No case at all because he was in my own house. In Jackson's own house, and Jackson had a right to kill him. But there's nothing that he did.'

Sophia felt for a moment like laughing lecherously. But somehow she just couldn't. She just couldn't.

Softly she asked, 'But you loved that boy, didn't you?'

Marta looked up through her tears. She looked at Sophia long before she decided that Sophia might understand.

Then just: 'Yes. The drunk woman's child has fallen.'

THE SUIT

Five-thirty in the morning, and the candlewick bedspread frowned as the man under it stirred. He did not like to wake his wife lying by his side — as yet — so he crawled up and out by careful peristalsis. But before he tip-toed out of his room with shoes and socks under his arm, he leaned over and peered at the sleeping serenity of his wife: to him a daily matutinal miracle.

He grinned and yawned simultaneously, offering his wordless *Te Deum* to whatever gods for the goodness of life; for the pure beauty of his wife; for the strength surging through his willing body; for the even, unperturbed rhythms of his passage through days and months and years — it must be — to heaven.

Then he slipped soundlessly into the kitchen. He flipped aside the curtain of the kitchen window, and saw outside a thin drizzle, the type that can soak one to the skin, and that could go on for days and days. He wondered, head aslant, why the rain in Sophiatown always came in the morning when workers had to creep out of their burrows; and then at how blistering heat-waves came during the day when messengers had to run errands all over; and then at how the rain came back when workers knocked off and had to scurry home.

He smiled at the odd caprice of the heavens, and tossed his head at the naughty incongruity, as if, 'Ai, but the gods!'

From behind the kitchen door he removed an old rain cape, peeling off in places, and swung it over his head. He dashed for the lavatory, nearly slipping in a pool of muddy water, but he reached the door. Aw, blast, someone had made it before him. Well, that is the toll of staying in a yard where twenty . . . thirty other people have to share the same lean-to. He was dancing and burning in that climactic moment when trousers-fly will not come wide soon enough. He stepped round the lavatory and watched the streamlets of rainwater quickly wash away the jet of tension that spouted from him. That infinite after-relief. Then he dashed back to his kitchen. He grabbed the old baby bath-tub hanging on a nail under the slight shelter of the gutterless roof-edge. He opened a large wooden box and quickly filled the bath-tub with coal. Then he inched his way back to the kitchen door and hurried inside.

He was huh-huh-huhing one of those fugitive tunes that cannot be hidden, but that often just occur and linger naggingly in the head. The fire he was making soon licked up cheerfully, in mood with his contentment.

He had a trick for these morning chores. While the fire in the old stove warmed up, the kettle humming on it, he gathered and laid ready the things he would need for the day: briefcase and the files that go with it; the book that he was currently reading; the letters of his lawyer boss which he usually posted before he

reached the office; his wife's and his own dry-cleaning
slips for the Sixty-Minutes; his lunch tin solicitously
prepared the night before by his attentive wife; and
today, the battered rain cape. When the kettle on the
stove began to sing (before it actually boiled), he
poured water into a wash basin, refilled and replaced
it on the stove. Then he washed himself carefully:
across the eyes, under, in and out the armpits, down
the torso and in between the legs. This ritual was
thorough, though no white man a-complaining of the
smell of wogs, knows anything about it. Then he
dressed himself fastidiously. By this time he was
ready to prepare breakfast.

Breakfast! How he enjoyed taking in a tray of
warm breakfast to his wife, cuddled in bed. To appear
there in his supreme immaculacy, tray in hand when
his wife came out of ether to behold him. These
things we blacks want to do for our own . . . not
fawningly for the whites for whom we bloody-well
got to do it. He denied that he was one of those who
believed in putting your wife in her place even if she
was a good wife. Not he.

Matilda, too, appreciated her husband's kindness,
and only put her foot down when he would offer to
wash up.

'Off with you,' she would scold him on his way.

At the bus-stop he was a little sorry to see that
jovial old Maphikela was in a queue for a bus ahead
of him. Today he would miss Maphikela's raucous
laughter and uninhibited, bawdy conversations in
fortissimo. Maphikela hailed him nevertheless. He
thought he noticed hesitation in the old man, and a
slight clouding of his countenance, but the old man
shouted back at him, saying that he would wait for
him at the terminus in town.

Philemon considered this morning trip to town with garrulous old Maphikela as his daily bulletin. All the township news was generously reported by loud-mouthed heralds, and spiritedly discussed by the bus at large. Of course, 'news' included views on bosses (scurrilous), the Government (rude), Ghana and Russia (idolatrous), America and the West (sympathetically ridiculing), and boxing (bloodthirsty). But it was always stimulating and surprisingly comprehensive for so short a trip. And there was no law of libel.

Maphikela was standing under one of those token bus-stop shelters that keep out neither rain nor wind nor sun-heat. Philemon easily located him by his noisy ribbing of some office boys in their khaki-green uniforms. They walked together into town, but from Maphikela's suddenly subdued manner, Philemon gathered that there was something serious coming up. Maybe a loan.

Eventually, Maphikela came out with it.

'Son,' he said sadly, 'if I could've avoided this, believe you me I would, but my wife is nagging the spice out of my life for not talking to you about it.'

It just did not become blustering old Maphikela to sound so grave and Philemon took compassion upon him.

'Go ahead, dad,' he said generously. 'You know you can talk to me about anything.'

The old man gave a pathetic smile. 'We-e-ell, it's not really any of our business . . . er . . . but my wife felt . . . you see. Damn it all! I wish these women would not snoop around so much.' Then he rushed it. 'Anyway, it seems there's a young man who's going to visit your wife every morning . . . ah . . . for these last bloomin' three months. And that wife of mine swears by her heathen gods you don't know a thing about it.'

It was not like the explosion of a devastating bomb. It was more like the critical breakdown in an infinitely delicate piece of mechanism. From outside the machine just seemed to have gone dead. But deep in its innermost recesses, menacing electrical flashes were leaping from coil to coil, and hot, viscous molten metal was creeping upon the fuel tanks . . . .

Philemon heard gears grinding and screaming in his head . . . .

'Dad,' he said hoarsely, 'I . . . I have to go back home.'

He turned around and did not hear old Maphikela's anxious, 'Steady, son. Steady, son.'

The bus ride home was a torture of numb dread and suffocating despair. Though the bus was now emptier Philemon suffered crushing claustrophobia. There were immense washerwomen whose immense bundles of soiled laundry seemed to baulk and menace him. From those bundles crept miasmata of sweaty intimacies that sent nauseous waves up and down from his viscera. The wild swaying of the bus as it negotiated Mayfair Circle hurtled him sickeningly from side to side. Some of the younger women shrieked delightedly to the driver, *'Fuduga! . . . Stir the pot!'* as he swung his steering wheel this way and that. Normally, the crazy tilting of the bus gave him a prickling exhilaration. But now . . . .

He felt like getting out of there, screamingly, elbowing everything out of his way. He wished this insane trip were over, and then again, he recoiled at the thought of getting home. He made a tremendous resolve to gather in all the torn, tingling threads of his nerves contorting in the raw. By a merciless act of

will, he kept them in subjugation as he stepped from
the bus back in the Victoria Road terminus, Sophiatown.

The calm he achieved was tense . . . but he could
think now . . . he could take a decision . . . .

With almost boyishly innocent urgency, he rushed
through his kitchen into his bedroom. In the lightning
flash that the eye can whip, he saw it all . . . the man
beside his wife . . . the chestnut arm around her neck
. . . the ruffled candlewick bedspread . . . the suit
across the chair. But he affected not to see.

He opened the wardrobe door, and as he dug into
it, he cheerfully spoke to his wife. 'Fancy, Tilly, I
forgot to take my pass. I had already reached town,
and was going to walk up to the office. If it hadn't
been for wonderful old Mr Maphikela . . . .

A swooshing noise of violent retreat and the clap
of his bedroom window stopped him. He came from
behind the wardrobe door and looked out from the
open window. A man clad only in vest and under-
pants was running down the street. Slowly, he turned
round and contemplated . . . the suit.

Philemon lifted it gingerly under his arm and
looked at the stark horror in Matilda's eyes. She was
now sitting up in bed. Her mouth twitched, but her
throat raised no words.

'Ha,' he said. 'I see we have a visitor,' indicating the
blue suit. 'We really must show some of our hospitality.
But first, I must phone my boss to tell him that I can't
come to work today . . . mmmm-er, my wife's not
well. Be back in a moment, then we can make arrange-
ments.' He took the suit along.

When he returned he found Matilda weeping on the
bed. He dropped the suit beside her, pulled up the
chair, turned it round so that its back came in front

of him, sat down, brought down his chin on to his folded arms before him, and waited for her.

After a while the convulsions of her shoulders ceased. She saw a smug man with an odd smile and meaningless inscrutability in his eyes. He spoke to her with very little noticeable emotion; if anything, with a flutter of humour.

'We have a visitor, Tilly.' His mouth curved ever so slightly. 'I'd like him to be treated with the greatest of consideration. He will eat every meal with us and share all we have. Since we have no spare room, he'd better sleep in here. But the point is, Tilly, that you will meticulously look after him. If he vanishes or anything else happens to him . . . ' a shaft of evil shot from his eye . . . 'Matilda, I'll kill you.'

He rose from the chair and looked with incongruous supplication at her. He told her to put the fellow in the wardrobe for the time being. As she passed him to get the suit, he turned to go. She ducked frantically, and he stopped.

'You don't seem to understand me, Matilda. There's to be no violence in this house if you and I can help it. So just look after that suit.' He went out.

He made his way to the Sophiatown Post Office, which is placed exactly on the line between Sophiatown and the white man's surly Westdene. He posted his boss's letters and walked to the beerhall at the tail end of Western Native Township. He had never been inside it before, but somehow the thunderous din laved his bruised spirit. He stayed there all day.

He returned home for supper . . . and surprises. His dingy little home had been transformed, and the air of stern masculinity it had hitherto contained had been wiped away, to be replaced by anxious feminine touches here and there. There were even gay, colour-

ful curtains swirling in the kitchen window. The old-
fashioned coal stove gleamed in its blackness. A clean,
chequered oil cloth on the table. Supper ready.

Then she appeared in the doorway of the bedroom.
Heavens! here was the woman he had married; the
young, fresh, cocoa-coloured maid who had sent
rushes of emotion shuddering through him. And the
dress she wore brought out all the girlishness of her,
hidden so long beneath German print. But no hint of
coquettishness, although she stood in the doorway
and slid her arm up the jamb, and shyly slanted her
head to the other shoulder. She smiled weakly.

'What makes a woman like this experiment with
adultery?' he wondered.

Philemon closed his eyes and gripped the seat of
his chair on both sides as some overwhelming, un-
disciplined force sought to catapult him towards her.
For a moment some essence glowed fiercely within
him, then sank back into itself and died . . . .

He sighed and smiled sadly back at her. 'I'm
hungry, Tilly.'

The spell snapped, and she was galvanized into
action. She prepared his supper with dexterous hands
that trembled a little when they hesitated in mid-air.
She took her seat opposite him, regarded him curiously, clasped her hands waiting for his prayer, but in her
heart she murmured some other, much more urgent
prayer of her own.

'Matilda!' he barked. 'Our visitor!' The sheer
savagery with which he cracked at her jerked her up,
but only when she saw the brute cruelty in his face
did she run out of the room, toppling the chair
behind her.

She returned with the suit on a hanger, and stood
there quivering like a feather. She looked at him with

helpless dismay. The demoniacal rage in his face was
evaporating, but his heavy breathing still rocked his
thorax above the table, to and fro.

'Put a chair there,' he indicated with a languid
gesture of his arm. She moved like a ghost as she drew
a chair to the table.

'Now seat our friend at the table . . . no, no, not
like that. Put him in front of the chair, and place him
on the seat so that he becomes indeed the third
person.'

Philemon went on relentlessly. 'Dish up for him.
Generously. I imagine he hasn't had a morsel all day,
the poor devil.'

Now, as consciousness and thought seeped back
into her, her movements revolved so that always she
faced this man who had changed so spectacularly. She
started when he rose to open the window and let in
some air.

She served the suit. The act was so ridiculous that
she carried it out with a bitter sense of humiliation
He came back to sit down and plunged into his meal.
No grace was said for the first time in this house.
With his mouth full, he indicated by a toss of his head
that she should sit down in her place. She did so.
Glancing at her plate, the thought occurred to her
that someone, after a long famine, was served a
sumptuous supper, but as the food reached her
mouth it turned to sawdust. Where had she heard it?

Matilda could not eat. She suddenly broke into
tears.

Philemon took no notice of her weeping. After
supper he casually gathered the dishes and started
washing up. He flung a dry cloth at her without
saying a word. She rose and went to stand by his side
drying up. But for their wordlessness, they seemed a

very devoted couple.

After washing up, he took the suit and turned to
her. 'That's how I want it every meal, every day.'
Then he walked into the bedroom.

So it was. After that first breakdown, Matilda
began to feel that her punishment was not too severe,
considering the heinousness of the crime. She tried
to put a joke into it, but by slow, unconscious
degrees, the strain nibbled at her. Philemon did not
harass her much more, so long as the ritual with the
confounded suit was conscientiously followed.

Only once, he got one of his malevolent brain-
waves. He got it into his head that 'our visitor' needed
an outing. Accordingly the suit was taken to the dry-
cleaners during the week, and, come Sunday, they
had to take it out for a walk. Both Philemon and
Matilda dressed for the occasion. Matilda had to carry
the suit on its hanger over her back and the three of
them strolled leisurely along Ray Street. They passed
the church crowd in front of the famous Anglican
Mission of Christ the King. Though the worshippers
saw nothing unusual in them, Matilda felt, searing
through her, red-hot needles of embarrassment, and
every needle-point was a public eye piercing into her
degradation.

But Philemon walked casually on. He led her down
Ray Street and turned into Main Road. He stopped
often to look into shop windows or to greet a friend
passing by. They went up Toby Street, turned into
Edward Road, and back home. To Philemon the
outing was free of incident, but to Matilda it was one
long, excruciating experience.

At home, he grabbed a book on Abnormal Psychology, flung himself into a chair and calmly said
to her, 'Give the old chap a rest, will you, Tilly?'

In the bedroom, Matilda said to herself that things could not go on like this. She thought of how she could bring the matter to a head with Philemon; have it out with him once and for all. But the memory of his face, that first day she had forgotten to entertain the suit; stayed with her. She thought of running away, but where to? Home? What could she tell her old-fashioned mother had happened between Philemon and her? All right, run away clean then. She thought of many young married girls who were divorcees now, who had won their freedom.

What had happened to Staff Nurse Kakile? The woman drank heavily now, and when she got drunk, the boys of Sophiatown passed her around and called her the Cesspot.

Matilda shuddered.

An idea struck her. There were still decent, married women around Sophiatown. She remembered how after the private schools had been forced to close with the introduction of Bantu Education, Father Harringay of the Anglican Mission had organized cultural clubs. One, she seemed to remember, was for married women. If only she could lose herself in some cultural activity, find absolution for her conscience in some club doing good; that would blur her blasted home life, would restore her self-respect. After all, Philemon had not broadcast her disgrace abroad . . . nobody knew; not one of Sophiatown's slander-mongers suspected how vulnerable she was. She must go and see Mrs Montjane about joining a cultural club. She must ask Philemon now if she might . . . she must ask him nicely.

She got up and walked into the other room where Philemon was reading quietly. She dreaded disturbing him, did not know how to begin talking to him . . .

they had talked so little for so long. She went and stood in front of him, looking silently upon his deep concentration. Presently he looked up with a frown on his face.

Then she dared. 'Phil, I'd like to join one of those cultural clubs for married women. Would you mind?'

He wrinkled his nose and rubbed it between thumb and index finger as he considered the request. But he had caught the note of anxiety in her voice and thought he knew what it meant.

'Mmmmm,' he said, nodding. 'I think that's a good idea. You can't be moping around here all day. Yes, you may, Tilly.' Then he returned to his book.

The cultural club idea was wonderful. She found women like herself, with time (if not with tragedy) on their hands, engaged in wholesome, refreshing activities. The atmosphere was cheerful and cathartic. They learned things and they did things. They organized fêtes, bazaars, youth activities, sport, music, self-help and community projects. She got involved in committees, meetings, debates, conferences. It was for her a whole new venture into humancraft, and her personality blossomed. Philemon gave her all the latitude she wanted.

Now, abiding by that silly ritual at home seemed a little thing . . . a very little thing . . . .

Then one day she decided to organize a little party for her friends and their husbands. Philemon was very decent about it. He said it was all right. He even gave her extra money for it. Of course, she knew nothing of the strain he himself suffered from his mode of castigation.

There was a week of hectic preparation. Philemon stepped out of its cluttering way as best he could. So many things seemed to be taking place simultaneously.

New dresses were made. Cakes were baked, three
different orders of meat prepared; beef for the
uninvited chancers; mutton for the normal guests;
turkey and chicken for the inner pith of the club's
core. To Philemon, it looked as if Matilda planned to
feed the multitude on the Mount with no aid of
miracles.

On the Sunday of the party Philemon saw Matilda's
guests. He was surprised by the handsome grace with
which she received them. There was a long table with
enticing foods and flowers and serviettes. Matilda
placed all her guests round the table, and the party
was ready to begin in the mock-formal township
fashion. Outside a steady rumble of conversation
went on where the human odds and ends of every
Sophiatown party had their 'share'.

Matilda caught the curious look on Philemon's
face. He tried to disguise his edict when he said, 'Er
. . . the guest of honour.'

But Matilda took a chance. She begged, 'Just this
once, Phil.'

He became livid. 'Matilda!' he shouted. 'Get our
visitor!' Then with incisive sarcasm, 'or are you
ashamed of him?'

She went ash-grey; but there was nothing for it but
to fetch her albatross. She came back and squeezed
a chair into some corner, and placed the suit on it.
Then she slowly placed a plate of food before it. For
a while the guests were dumbfounded. Then curiosity
flooded in. They talked at the same time. 'What's
the idea, Philemon? . . . Why must she serve a suit?
. . . What's happening?' Some just giggled in a silly
way. Philemon carelessly swung his head towards
Matilda. 'You better ask my wife. She knows the
fellow best.'

All interest beamed upon poor Matilda. For a moment she could not speak, all-enveloped in misery. Then she said, unconvincingly, 'It's just a game that my husband and I play at mealtime.' They roared with laughter. Philemon let her get away with it.

The party went on, and every time Philemon's glare sent Matilda scurrying to serve the suit each course; the guests were no-end amused by the persistent mock-seriousness with which this husband and wife played out their little game. Only, to Matilda, it was no joke; it was a hot poker down her throat. After the party, Philemon went off with one of the guests who had promised to show him a joint 'that sells genuine stuff, boy, genuine stuff.'

Reeling drunk, late that sabbath, he crashed through his kitchen door, onwards to his bedroom. Then he saw her.

They have a way of saying in the argot of Sophiatown, 'Cook out of the head!' signifying that someone was impacted with such violent shock that whatever whiffs of alcohol still wandered through his head were instantaneously evaporated and the man stood sober before stark reality.

There she lay, curled, as if just before she died she begged for a little love, implored some implacable lover to cuddle her a little . . . just this once . . . just this once more.

In intense anguish, Philemon cried, 'Tilly!'

THE URCHIN

One sling of the braces would not keep up on the shoulder, just like one worm of pale-green mucus kept crawling down the chestnut lip and would suddenly dart back like a timid creature. But ten-year old Macala wore his long pants (surely someone's castaway three-quarter jeans) with a defiant pride just ready to assault the rest of the known world. Other boys his age had only had short pants.

He looked up and down from Mafuta's Chinaman store along Victoria Road, Sophiatown, and he thought of how his day ought to begin. Mafuta's was not good: he kept two very ferocious dogs in his shop, and fairly authenticated rumour had it that he also kept a gun that made a terrible noise. But the vistas up and down Victoria Road offered infinite possibilities for a man. To the left there were queues upon queues of half-frightened, half-foolish people who simply asked to be teased. Then Moosa's store with all those fruity, sweet things in the window; but they said Moosa trained at night with irons. Opposite, across from Millar Street, there was a Chink butcher, but his counter was fenced off with wire,

and ooh! those cruel knives and hatchets. There must
be a lot of money there for it to be protected so
formidably. And next to the butcher, the bicycle
shop with its blaring juke-box: Too roo roo roo tu!
Too roo roo roo tu-tu! Here where a passerby girl
would suddenly break into a dance step, seductive
beyond her years.

All like that, up to Chang's, and from there just the
denuded places the demolition squad had left in
Sophiatown.

To the right, Macala stared at Benghali House. The
only double-storey building in the whole of Sophiatown. In front of it all sorts of pedlars meet: sweet-
potato sellers, maize-sellers, sugar-cane sellers, African
pimpled-squash sellers, shoe-lace sellers — all of whom
couldn't care whether or not the shopkeeper alone
held a licence to sell any of these goods.

Macala's eyes glittered as he saw the Ma-Ndebele
women squatting in their timeless patience behind
their huge dishes of maize-cobs, dried morogo, peanut
cubes, wild fruits like morula, ditlhatswa, mmupudu
— things the urban African never sees on trees these
days.

To Macala, these women with their quaint and
beaded necks and legs that made them look like
colourful pythons, were the fairest game.

He stepped off the veranda of Mafuta's shop, off
the pavement, and sauntered swaggeringly towards
these placid women in front of Benghali House. He
was well aware that the street-corner loungers,
enormous liars all of them, were watching him,
thinking that the slightest move by Macala promised
excitement and trouble.

He stopped in front of a Ndebele woman transfixed to her white dish, as if she were one with it, and

as if trade meant just being there at the strategic place
and time: no bawling, no bartering, no bargaining.

'Dis — how much?' and that to Macala was English
with a vengeance. She looked up at him with large,
baffled eyes, but before she spoke Macala lifted his
foot and trod on the edge of the dish, sending its
contents churning into the dust of Victoria Road's
pavement. He shrieked with delight as he ran off.

What she hurled at him in virulent Ndebele may
have been curses, prayers, lamentations. But to
Macala it was reward enough, the kind of thing that
proves the superiority of the townsman over these
odd creatures from the country. The passing
generation's men and women shook their heads and
muttered gloomily: 'The children of today, the
children of today.'

His momentum took him to the vegetable vendor
just opposite Mafuta's. In a fluid movement he seized
the handle of the cart and whirled it round and up for
the devil of it. Potatoes, onions, pumpkins, cabbages
went swirling into the air and plump tomatoes
squashed on the tarmac. The khaki-coated vendor
stood aghast a second before he broke into impre-
cations that shuddered even the sordid Sophiatown
atmosphere. But Macala was away on his mischievous
path.

He had passed the 'Fish and Chips' too fast for
another tilt, and met his pals on the corner of Tucker
and Victoria: Dipapang, Jungle and Boy-Boy. Together
they should have been 'Our Gang' but their organisation was not tight enough for that.

Boy-Boy's was the brain that germinated most of
the junior devilry of the team, but he did not quite
have Macala's impetuous courage of execution. He
looked like a social worker's explanation of 'conditions

in the slums': thin to malnourished, delinquent, un-
disciplined, dedicated to a future gallows. Yet his
father was an important man and his mother a
teacher. Jungle qualified by the ease with which he
could talk of using a knife. In real big-tsotsi fashion.
Dipapang initiated nothing, thought nothing, was
nothing, but was always so willing to join in, to
try and finish anything the others cared to start.

'Heit, Macacix!' called Boy-Boy. 'It's how there?'

Macala suddenly felt in the mood for the jargon of
the townships. The near-animal, amorphous, quick-
shifting lingo that alarms farm-boys and drives cops
to all branches of suspicion; but which marks the city
slicker who can cope with all its vagaries.

'It's couvert under the corzet,' Macala replied,
bobbing his head this way and that to the rhythm.

'Hai man, bigshot, you must be the reely-reely
outlaw in this town,' Boy-Boy parried and lunged.

'Naw,' Macala feinted, 'dis town, Softtown's too
small for me. I'll take Western and Corrie and Maclera
and London, and smash them into a mash potato.'

Boy-Boy fell for it. 'Whew!' he whistled, 'don't say
you'll crowd me out!'

Macala took him by the throat and went in for the
kill. 'Didn't I tell you, buster, to keep out of my
country, or else . . . . '

He proceeded to carry out the menacing 'or else'
by choking Boy-Boy and slowly tripping him over a
leg he had slipped behind him until they rolled over
as Boy-Boy fell and tumbled into the gutter.

Boy-Boy gasped: 'Ah give up, boss, da country's
yours.'

The mock battle was over and everybody laughed
. . . except Jungle. He was reputed to be 'serious' and
that meant he was of the homicidal type. He sat there

on the storm water drain with his mournful face, sharpening gratingly on the concrete his Three Star jack-knife which from some hazy movie memory he called his 'gurkha'. As the laughter trailed off, he suddenly drawled: 'Have you guys heard that Mpedi was arrested yesterday?'

They stared at him in genuine stupefaction. Then Boy-Boy said: 'Yerrrr! How'd it happen, Jungle?'

But Jungle was not one for elaborating a story. Very unsatisfactorily, he said: 'Waal, he was drinking at de English Lady's joint . . . and . . . and dey got him.'

'You mean he didn't shoot it out? You mean dey took him just like dat? But I bet ya dey couldn't put handcuffs on Mpedi!' But Macala was very unhappy about the tame way in which the idol of the township was arrested.

Boy-Boy it was who made a story of it. 'Yerrr! But there is an outee.' He rose from the pavement and stood before the fascinated gaze of his pals. He stuck his thumbs into his belt and swayed his hips as he strutted up and down before them. Then he mimicked the bull-brained fearlessness of Mpedi, the mirror and form of almost all young Sophiatown, the clattering terror of men, and the perennial exasperation of the police station across the road.

'Ya! Da room was full — full to da door. Clevers, bigshots, boozers, bamboos, coat-hangers, hole-diggers and bullets, blondes, figure eights and capital l's, wash-planks and two-ton trucks. Da boys were in da stack and da dames were game . . . .

'Then Bura Mpedi stepped in, his eyes blood-red. The house went dead-still. Ag, man, Bura Mpedi, man. He stood there and looked left . . . and looked right . . . his man was not there. He stepped in some more. The house was dead. He grabbed a beer from the nearest table and slugged it from the bottle. Who would talk?' Boy-Boy's upper lip curled up on one side in utter contempt. 'He, who would talk!'

Macala and his pals were caught in Boy-Boy's electric pause. Even Jungle was aroused by this dramatic display of township bullycraft.

Boy-Boy's histrionics continued: 'Yerrrr! a drunk girl came from under a table, and tried Mpedi for a drink. "Au, Bura Mpedi, give me a beer." Bura Mpedi put a boot on her shoulder and pushed her back under da table. Hai, man, hai man, dat outee is coward-cool, man. And he hates cherry coat-hangers. But dat night his eyes were going all over looking for Mahlalela. Yeffies! If he'd caught Mahlalela dat night . . . !'

Lifted by the wide-eyed admiration of his pals, Boy-Boy went on to surpass himself. He flung out his right arm recklessly, and declared: 'But dat's nutting yet! You should have seen Bura Mpedi when dey sent four lean cops to come and take him. Payroll robbery, Booysens . . . one thousand pound! Assault with GBH, Newlands . . . three men down and out! House-breakin' 'n Thatha . . . Lower Houghton!

'Dey came, man dey came. Four cops, two had guns, two had small inches. Dey surrounded da joint in Gibson Street, and dey called out to him to give up. Dey didn't know Mpedi with moonwash in his brains and a human intestine round his waist. He drew his point-three-five and his forty-five, and he came out shooting: Twah! Twah! Twah! Da two cops with small inches ducked into a shebeen nearby and ordered themselves a ha' nip brandy. One with da gun ran down Gibson Street for reinforces. Da last cop took a corner and decided to shoot it out with Mpedi.

But da bullets came so fast he never got a chance to poke out a shot.

'Hee-e-e, I tell you Mpedi was da outce.' Then, still carried forward by the vibrance of his enthusiasm, Boy-Boy rounded off his dramatisation by backing away slowly as he fired off imaginary guns, and barked: 'Twah! Twah! Twah!'

But the elation that had swelled up in Macala was now shot through with envy. 'How come,' he grumbled, 'da cops got him so easy now?' Yet what really worried him was that he knew how far he was beneath the fabulous Mpedi; that even in his own weight division he could not make such an awe-inspiring impression. He was not even as good an actor as Boy-Boy to recount and represent the exploits of the almighties. He looked at Boy-Boy bitterly and told himself: I'll beat his brains out if he gets smart with me.

It was Jungle who wrenched him out of his sour reverie. 'Boys, I think we should go finish off da Berliners,' he said prosaically.

A flash of fear leapt into Boy-Boy's eyes, for he knew this meant war. Macala was himself a bit scared, but seeing the fear in Boy-Boy, he screwed his heart through a hole too small for it.

And Jungle's 'gurkha' went on scraping the pavement concrete, screech-screech! screech-screech!

'Come ahn, let's go,' Macala suddenly decided.

They swaggered along Victoria Road, filling it from pavement to pavement as if they were a posse. Silent. Full of purpose. Deliberately grim. Boys and girls scampered for cover. Grown-ups stepped discreetly out of their way. Only the bigger tsotsis watched them with pride, and shouted encouragements like: 'Da men who rule da town!' and 'Tomorrow's outees!'

On the corner of Meyer Street they broke up a
ring of young dicers and forced them to join up.
Along the way they collected non-schoolgoing loafers
who lounged against shop walls; blue jeaned youngsters who twisted the arms of schoolgirls in rough
love; odd-job boys who ran errands for shopkeepers;
truants, pickpockets, little thugs within their age
limit — the lot.

By the time they turned into Edith Street, they
were a miniature army of hell-bent ruffians. Macala
led them and felt the strange thrill of the force
behind him. He chose Edith Street because it rose
into a rocky hill with plenty of stones for ammuni-
tion, and dropped suddenly into that part of Sophiatown they called Berlin where the walls were smeared
with crude swastikas.

Macala split his men into two groups. Those with
thick, bronze-buckle belts were to go under Jungle's
command through a gap in the row of houses precariously perched on huge boulders.

The excitement chopped Macala's breath into
dollops as he gave out his instructions. 'You boys get
dem from de back. You start de war. When dey come
running up Edward Road, dey'll meet us. Use dat
butcher of yours Uncle Jungle.'

Jungle gave one of his rare smiles, and his men
took position.

Macala and his group, first placing a sentinel on the
hill-top, slowly clambered down the rocks and waited
for Jungle to get around.

Though he was going into the den of the enemy,
Jungle did not find it difficult to rout them. There
was a biggish group of them playing dice in the usual
ring, and when he swooped upon them, they instinct-

ively thought it was the police and dashed up Edward Road, sticks and buckle belts raining on their heads.

Jungle himself had chosen a heftily-built fellow and was stabbing at him as he ran. Boy-Boy was later to describe it graphically: 'Yerrr! dat guy just wouldn't fall. Jungle had him — zip! But he ran on. Jungle caught him again in the neck — zip! He stumbled and trotted on his hands and feet. Jungle got him in the buttock — zip! But, yerrrr! he just wouldn't fall.'

Before the Berliners could rally and make a stand, they had run into Macala's stone-throwing division. Though it was very one-sided, the fight became fierce. The Berliners were now fighting, and because they were trapped and because they had to fight with their bare hands most of the time, they became young devils from the playgrounds of hell.

Stones and all sorts of other missiles were hurled in all directions. Knives were brandished and plunged, big-buckled belts were swung in whistling arcs, arms were flailed in the centre of the imbroglio with desperate savagery. Women screamed, shops closed, traffic diverted itself. Now and then a blood-spattered boy would stagger off the street to a house wall just to sit down and watch. Too done in to flee.

Then suddenly came the shrill warning cry, 'Arrara! Arrarayii!' The action stopped almost as abruptly as those ancient films which froze in mid-motion and transfixed the movement into a photograph. And just as suddenly afterwards, they all scattered pell-mell. When the police van came round the corner, it was impossible to decide who to pursue. For now, every-body was running up and down and off the streets. The scores of small boys, ordinary pedestrians who had just arrived upon the scene, fah-fee runners with

full-blown cheeks a-chumping the incriminating
tickets of their illicit lottery; everybody was running.
In Sophiatown you do not stop to explain to the
police that you had nothing to do with it; or that you
knew some of the culprits and could help the police.

The mobile squad were satisfied with merely
clearing the street.

Breathless and bruised, Macala found himself at the
open commonage called Macauvlei, adjacent to Waterval Hospital which served as the waste dumps to
the city, and 'golf course' to those Africans who went
in for the sport of leisure. Macala knew that most of
his gang would sooner or later find their way there.
He sat on a mound of ash, gasping heavily.

By the time Boy-Boy had arrived he had regained
his breath and was pitching chalky, burnt-out pebbles
rather pointlessly. Jungle came, for once, apparently,
in his seventh heaven. Dipapang too, grinned happily
though his shirt had been torn down and hung from
his body. A few other stragglers from the Black Caps
joined them, and then came the news. News that
oddly took the shape of 'They say'.

'Dey say,' announced one urchin, 'dat one of de
Berliners is dead.'

Stultifying fright seized them all. One small boy
simply broke out crying. Macala had trouble with a
choking clod in his throat.

'Dey say,' came in another boy, 'de Berliners are
going to call in de Big Berliners.'

'Agh,' grunted Macala in contempt. 'We'll go 'n tell
Bura Shark.'

'Dey say de cops're going to round us all up tonight.'

Despite all their bravado, all their big-shot stances
and their blistering contempt for cops and the law,

there is one thing that this knighthood really fears,
and it was expressed by a crackling of interjections
from each according to his own lights: 'Six lashes and
reformatory!'

'De cane and off to a farm!'

'Cuts with a light cane and no fine!'

Someone elaborated the procedure by filling in the
gory details: 'Dey say, two huge cops hold you down
over a big bench an' you got nothin' on. You can't
move. Now, maybe de magistrate he said: "Six cuts".
Dat's nothin'. If you cry, for every one you get two.
An' dose cops who give de lashes, dey train for you,
dey pick up weightlifting for you, dey grip a grip all
day for you. Den when de other cops got you on de
bench, an' you can't move, an' you don't want to cry,
de lashing cop he takes de cane, he swishes it over his
head, one — two — three, whish! De tattoo jumps up
on your buttocks.

'Dey say, he den goes to sit down, light a cigarette,
and talks with de other cops. Den he comes again.
One of de cops holding you turns your head so you
can see de lashing cop coming. He swishes de cane,
one-two-three, whish! 'Nother tattoo comes up, dis
time with blood. Red blood from your buttocks. He
goes for 'nother pull at his cigarette, or maybe he
looks for his tea dis time.

'He comes again. Dis time he sneezes his nose on
your buttocks, and makes jokes how black buttocks
is tough. He swishes de cane, one-two-three, whish! If
you don't cry, maybe you get your six lashes straight.
But if you cry, only *jus' Maye Babo!* Oh-ho-ho! . . .

'An' dey say, sometimes after you get lashes, six
days, two weeks you can't sit in de bus, you give your
seat to de aunties. Hai, dat cane dey keep in de salt
water when nobody get lashes!'

By that time the horror of the prospect had seeped through every delinquent soul. It was Macala who spoke first.

He said determinedly: 'Me, I'm not going home to-night.'

But Boy-Boy did not like the idea. He knew that his mother would not rest until she had found out where he was. Worse still, she might even go and ask the police to help her find him. 'Naw, Macacix, I'm going home. I don't want my ma to send cops looking for me. I don't like cops catching me when my ma is not there. I'm going home.'

As he walked away, the whole little gang suddenly broke up and walked home their different ways. As they scattered, Macala became frantic with panic. With consternation twisting his face, and his arms floating like a blind man's in front of him, he looked half comic as he stood on that mound of ash.

'Hey, hey, you guys, don't leave me alone. We're de boys . . . . '

He heard a sound of impatience behind him.

'Aargh! Let them go, Macala.' He turned round and reeled unsteadily as he saw Jungle standing there, not looking frightened at all.

'Wh-what you going to do, Jungle?'

Jungle took out his 'gurkha' and scraped it across his palm from left to right. Then he said: 'I'm going home, Macala,' and that mournful expression crept across his countenance. 'And when de cops come to get me tonight . . . . ' He made an ugly motion with his knife under his chin. He walked away with the slow, lanky movement of that gawky body of his.

By the time Macala decided to leave Macauvlei, it was getting dark. But he knew where he was going. Rather unnecessarily, he skulked along the fences of the street, looking this way and that. Now and then, he would be petrified by the zoom of a passing car or duck into an alley when headlights bored golden shafts through the dark of the street. But ultimately he reached the open space where Gerty, Bertha and Toby Streets used to be. He saw the dark building for which he was headed. He ran forward and stopped in front of it, but this side of the street. Slowly now. Somewhere here there is a night watchman, a Zulu with a thick black beard and barbel moustache, black uniform and black face that rubbed him out of sight in the dark, and a gnarled knobkerrie known to have split skulls.

But Macala knew where the corrugated-iron fence had snarled out a lip of entrance for him. He went on his hands and knees, and crawled away from the immense double gate towards this entrance. He found it and coiled himself inside. He knew there were stacks of corrugated iron in this timber yard, and if he touched them, the racket would alert the night watchman. So he did not go far, just nestled himself near his exit.

A little breeze was playing outside, hastening a piece of paper down the street, and now and then a bus or lorry would thunder by. But Macala slept, occasionally twitching in the hidden mechanics of sleep.

He was too far from where he could hear a woman's voice calling stridently: 'Mac-a-a-a-la! Mac-a-a-a-la! Hai, that child will one day bring me trouble.'

Journalism

TERROR IN THE TRAINS

Friday night, and the end of the month to boot. That's why, joining the hordes that flowed into Park Station, Johannesburg, Isaac Moeketsi of Dube — and thousands like him — was scared. He had, to a more intense degree, that sinking, uneasy feeling he always got when he had to board any of these location trains. More intense because he knew that robbers would be making that extra effort on this most special of nights.

Isaac had his pay packet in his inside coat pocket. Once on the train he would press his right arm against the pocket every now and then to make sure the money was still there. But he would do it in such a way that nobody would notice, he hoped.

Then he plunged into that throng. For him there was no safety in numbers. He knew that in this crowd were pickpockets, gangsters, robbers, hard-boiled thugs, beat-up men and even downright killers. Of course most of the people were just potential victims, but, Lord, who's who?

Maybe he'll make it home safely, or maybe he will be another bruised, battered, embittered hard-working man who tells his stunned wife: 'It's not even much good going to the police.' But there are thousands of others who know and understand his fear. For pay day is panic day for all of them. Mothers, wives, workers, even chance visitors.

Congestion on the trains has become virtually unbearable during peak hours. The few third-class coaches, the all too few trains, jam-packed with gasping frightened humanity — oh what a chance for their criminal stepbrothers.

There is little method in the operations of these criminals. Many pickpockets just put their hands into your pocket and take what they want. More likely as not you will not feel anything as you struggle for breath in the crowd. If you do, what matter? They out-brave you and threaten you with violence. The younger pickpockets go down on their knees, cut a hole into your trousers with a razor blade, and then let slide into their hands whatever comes forth.

But the true terror for train users comes from the rough-house thugs who hold people up at the point of a knife or gun, or simply rob and beat up passengers. The fear among passengers is so deep that some people don't even want to admit that they have been robbed. And pay days — Fridays, month-ends, from half-past four in the afternoon — are the devil's birthdays.

The other day we went to see for ourselves. We got to Park Station about 3 o'clock in the afternoon. People were already beginning to stream in. Almost everyone was in a hurry, and had an anxious expression. It was Friday again. Then we went through the barriers, down the steps, and into the swarms on the platform.

Flush on our arrival, plain-clothes policemen were

arresting a man for robbing somebody on the platform. They twisted him round, and pushed him off through some cursing people. The drama had begun. We let a few trains pass for we wanted to see how the people in this thick mass boarded them.

Wheee! In rushed an electric train. A man in brown overalls yelled the destination and the stops on the way, but his voice, already hoarse, couldn't rise above the din. People were jabbering at each other frantically, asking, 'Where is it going? Where does it stop?' Before everyone could get in, the train pulled out. Men and women were hanging precariously outside open doors, squeezing for all they were worth to get in. And the train slid out of sight. The same thing happened with every train.

We chanced a Dube train. It was packed, jammed like putty. On all sides humans were pressing against us. In the passage, between seats, on seat-backs — humans. Four on three-man seats, three on two-man seats. Crammed. One woman screamed for help because somebody pressed against her hard and her purse seemed to be sliding out of her pocket. At intermediate stations more and more people forced their way in.

At Phefeni Station many people got off, and we had some relief. As the train moved off, in a sparkling flash I saw a man poised on the platform like a baseball pitcher. Then he flung a missile. Crash! It struck a window. We all ducked. It looked as if he were doing it just out of spite. Maybe he'd tried to rob people in an earlier train and failed.

Nothing much happened for the rest of the trip — that is 'nothing' except periodic pickpocketing and stealing of parcels which we learned about later. On

our way back we met a man who was so drunk that
he didn't know he was being robbed. He got pushed
out of the train and landed on his back.

In the coach next to ours three thugs assaulted a
man who resisted their attempts to go through his
pockets. After this the other passengers were afraid to
resist the thugs, who robbed a few more people
before getting off the train.

We met a man whose suitcase was thrown out of a
window as the train passed a station. He had to get
off at the next station and come back to look for
it. Wonder of wonders! He found a woman who had
taken charge of the suitcase, and he got it back
intact. It happened in Johannesburg.

There are various gangs operating on trains or near
railway stations on the Reef. In the Moroka-Jabavu-
Mofolo area and in Pimville it is mainly the Torch
Gang. They specialise in 'Dark Patch' operations —
robberies in unlit areas just outside the stations.
Suddenly a man finds a torch flashed into his face,
blinding him for a moment. Then a stunning blow on
the head. Next thing he is lying in the grass, beaten
up and robbed.

In the Orlando area there is the Mlamlankunzi
Gang, a bunch of youngsters who work on the trains.
One will come from behind and give you an elbow
lock round the neck while another will point a knife
or a screwdriver to your belly, and then they rob you.
If you resist, they throw you out of the moving train.

There has been some violent reaction to these train robbers, and tsotsis in general, in the Dube area. Prop-eared
Zulus first ganged together to beat them up, the
reaction of harried people at the end of their tether.

But it then went all haywire. Some Zulus went about

hitting people indiscriminately. They have a saying, 'Hit a cap and a tsotsi will jump out.' So anybody who wore a cap was in danger of being clubbed. Recently they went even further, beating up old women in their homes after accusing them that, 'Your sons are tsotsis.' They smashed houses without having done the most elementary research.

Then a few weeks ago, the situation became electric, and the two main opposing tribes in the area poised themselves for violence. The Zulus, chiefly from Dube Hostel, and the Basotho, with reinforcements from as far as Evaton and Vereeniging, clashed during a bloody weekend of violence. They went at each other with murderous weapons, including battle axes. During three days about 40 people were killed and 100 injured. The police were kept busy day and night keeping the blood-mad warriors from each other, and sometimes the police were forced to shoot.

What caused this sudden violent explosion? In a certain sense it has not been a surprise to those of us who live in these townships. We have lived with terrorism so long that we have always feared that one day there would be an eruption. You can't live with assault, robbery and murder without something big happening eventually.

The situation has been aggravated, according to many people, by the policy of ethnic grouping, which has led the more tribal among us to think of other tribes as foreigners, enemies. We are not allowed to learn to live together in peace, say the train-using bus-boarding philosophers to whom the Dube wave of terror has become a matter of life and death.

The two sides are threatening to go on fighting until Christmas, which will become the Devil's Dance in this bloody affair. They must be stopped!

INSIDE DUBE HOSTEL

Dube Hostel is the place that nobody wants. The people who live in the bleak and forbidding buildings never wanted to go there. For many of them it is just a place to lay down a weary head, and a shelter from the dust or the rain. Lots of them are Johannesburg workers who were uprooted from their rooms in the city by the 'Locations in the Sky' Act. Their employers don't like it either. They say that things worked much more smoothly when the workers were nearby and didn't have long journeys to make every day.

The Advisory Board pinpoints the hostel as the cancer in an area that could have been peaceful. The Johannesburg City Council, too, believes it to be a source of the recent weekend of horror, when about 40 people were killed.

I spent a couple of nights in the hostel in the atmosphere of the riots and the fear that it has engendered — fear that paralysed men around me and communicated itself threateningly.

My first night at Dube was a Friday. The hostel was quiet. There were few people around. So many had fled away to relatives and friends in other townships; so many had gone to sleep in the city, in the very backyards from which they had been hounded.

Dube Hostel is a little colony of hall-like buildings fenced in by wire netting. The different tribes are separated. There is a building for the Sotho group, a set of buildings for the Nguni (Zulu, Xhosa, Swazi) group, another for the Venda-Shangaan group. That is what is meant by ethnic grouping. The tribes must be kept apart. This ethnic grouping has come in for quite a blast since the killings in Dube and Meadowlands.

The buildings are each partitioned into sections. One of the sections is used as a kitchen, but there are no stoves, no fire-places. There is a table on which food can be eaten or prepared. The bedrooms have hostel beds, and there is a locker for each inmate. People play draughts or cards on a bed.

So, in the hush of the night we talked about the fights. I was told that people in the area have for a long time been terrorised by tsotsis. In the trains, in the streets, in lonely, dark patches. Recently the tsotsis devised a new trick. First, they disguised themselves as Zulus, clipping little round rubber discs to their ears, and went about assaulting and robbing the Basotho.

When the Basotho got fed-up with these marauding 'Zulus', the tsotsis played the game of being 'Russians' — coloured-blanketed Basotho gangsters. Then they went to assault the Zulus of the hostel.

The bane of the situation was that ethnic grouping kept the tribes so apart that they could not get together and see through the tsotsis' ruse — even though they lived in the same hostel. When the attacks increased the Zulus decided to organise themselves for revenge.

But they did not, at first, deliberately go for the

Basotho. They thought they would remove the tsotsi menace first, and they went about hitting anybody who looked even remotely like a tsotsi.

Even in jokes, tribes have generalised their gibes at each other. There's come a song that says:

> *You give birth to a Mosotho,*
> *Then you give birth to a spy.*
> *You give birth to a Zulu,*
> *Then you give birth to a watchman.*
> *You give birth to a coloured,*
> *Then you give birth to a drunk.*
> *You give birth to a Xhosa,*
> *Then you give birth to a thief.*

But the Zulus generalised with their sticks, I was told. The tsotsis went one further. They actually wrote a letter that pretended to come from the Basotho — to the Zulus, challenging them to come out and fight. The Zulus came out, and fought in a big, rough way.

The Basotho, victims of the tsotsi ruse, naturally organised themselves for fighting back. They called for reinforcements from as far as Evaton and Vereeniging.

The night was silent as I listened to the people in the hostel tell me all this. We missed the heavy roar of tribal music that one hears in other hostels. And the dancing.

Here at Dube, all was a chilled stillness. Outside, the police were patrolling round the townships of Meadowlands, Dube and Phefeni in lorries, squad cars and riot cars.

We slept, and the following morning I joined the train of workers marching in sullen procession to the station.

'Dube Hostel must go!' thundered a man I met at the station. He was short, but powerfully built, and seemed one of those people who like quick decisions.

'We can't have on our doorstep a cage with people who live in herds; who don't live with women; who cook hit-and-run meals and have only a beer-yard for their nightly entertainment. Something had to break in a big way. Dube must go! We got daughters, you know.'

But it seemed that many people wanted the fight to go on. So the manager of the City Council's Non-European Affairs Department, Mr W J P Carr, got a number of African chiefs to tour the riot area and persuade their tribesmen to keep peace. One man, who described himself as a Congressite, shouted that the chiefs were talking rubbish.

There is still a fear that things will blow up at Christmas. That doesn't leave much time to set things right. The people in the area want peace and that means more than police protection. They want prevention.

WHY OUR LIVING'S SO TOUGH

There's a sticky problem that all of us have to settle now and again. It's stated in the groan of the workman who looked ruefully at his pay-packet and said: 'Pay day is the worst day, for then you have to pay for accounts greater than the pay.' Other people with fancy ways of putting things call it, 'The Problem of the Cost of Living'. Jokers have even mentioned the cost of dying. But for us it's the monthly nightmare, and has resolved itself into the question: 'How do we manage to eat at all?'

How decently are people paid, and how decently do they live? Let's see. A survey conducted by the Johannesburg Chamber of Commerce in 1957 concluded that a monthly income of £31 was the minimum necessary for adequate and decent living for a family of five in a Johannesburg African township. On the authority of *African Poverty* — a booklet published after investigations by the South African Institute of Race Relations between 1950 and 1956 — the average income of most families is £15. Or less than half the necessary minimum.

That is the heart of the matter. You need £31 a

month to live 'adequately and decently'. You get only £15 a month to do the job. So you don't live adequately and decently. There are some who get more. There are also the few who get less, who go further and further down as life goes on.

All along the way down come crude, insufficient substitutes. Tobacco rolls for cigarettes: late night street-roving for inadequate blanketing (if you sleep late you fall asleep faster during cold spells): fruit, milk, meat must give way for bleak porridge and *kaaings* — crackling; when the struggle gets too savage oh well, you get savage too.

What we've discovered in the lives of three families — especially the middle one — represent thousands of you, and you, and you. They represent among Non-Europeans the High, the Middle and the Low. Families that earn more that £30 a month; families that earn between £15 and £25 a month; and families that earn less than £15 a month.

In Matsemela Street, Western Township, Johannesburg, is the home of Mr and Mrs J D Radebe. The house is beautifully surrounded by a flower garden. Inside, flowers bedeck the table and walls in tasteful arrangement.

Mr Radebe earns £8 a week as a lorry driver for a chemical firm. His wife, Agnes, is a schoolteacher earning about £10 a month. They have five children, including sixteen-year-old John, who works in town. John's wages don't go to the support of the family.

The family pays £2 5s for rent. They have quite modern furniture, for which they are paying £3 a month hire-purchase.

They dress well, the children have the necessary toys and the family buys a number of local newspapers and periodicals.

The son goes for American fashions and expensive shoes. They eat meat daily, and seldom have hard porridge. Vegetables and fruit are part of their daily diet.

Looking at the gay, vivacious girls, the happy family life, and listening to Mr Radebe's friendly, back-slapping guffaws, I thought: 'To them that hath more shall be given . . . .'

That's a picture of a well-to-do family, not too far out in the skies, but living adequately and decently. But there is the other extreme, that of struggling, miserable humanity, even too bewildered to spread their meagre earnings systematically.

Directly opposite the Radebe household lives Mr Lucas Ndlovu's family of nine, supported mainly — but not entirely — by Lucas, who earns £2 12s 6d a week as an office cleaner in the city. They pay rent of £1 a month, and their dreary, unimproved house looks it.

Shabbines has sprinkled itself in dust all over the house. The one room we entered — the 'front' room — had an odd collection of tables and chairs, and was a bedroom-cum-kitchen. During the many times that I visited them I never felt any heat coming from the stove. Lucas's three children have no toys, not even at Christmas.

Life for the Ndlovus is an iron-grey, cheerless, frightening affair with the first generation gloomily waiting for the end; the second generation darting back and forth to snatch furtive and frightened excitements; and the child generation with no promise save God's chance miracle, or poised precariously on the edge of delinquency at the end of the street.

But the bulk group is represented by what I have intrepidly called the Middle Class. I should have labelled them the Hit-Or-Miss Class. For some people it's confused Africa, for others it's Sane Africa, the Hope, for most of us it's the border and south of the border.

The case of Simon Ngubeni, of White City, Jabavu, will show you. He himself earns £3 7s 6d a week, working in a bakery. His wife, Makoti — it really means 'daughter-in-law' — does not work because she has household chores and a seven-month-old baby to look after. But his mother, Maria Ngubeni, 45, fetches washing, does it at home, and gets about 18s a week. In his spare-time, Simon does rent-collecting for an Alexandra landlord, and on that he makes about 15s a week, which comes once a month. They spend between £2 to £3 a week on food.

There are three children in the family; two at school, the other a baby of six months.

Simon is a man of sober habits. He has his occasional draught of KB at friendly parties on weekends. Even then he does not spend more than 2s per party. But for a family whose total income is £15 16s 6d a month, life is not something you can laugh back at.

Theirs is the ordinary kind of middle-class family you get in the township. The furniture is ordinary, plain almost. They have two rooms, a kitchen and sitting-room-bedroom. No electricity, they use candles. The women; wife and mother, sew most of the clothing. The kids often have to go to school without shoes because they must save the one pair each has for rare occasions.

They can't afford to eat meat daily. On other days they have to resort to pumpkin leaves, which make a handy spinach, or samp mixed with fat or sour milk. Vegetables come on special days. They have to budget strictly to live as they are doing now. They live, but just barely.

The husband seldom goes out to entertainments or socials with his family (but occasionally on his own to a good movie he has heard about, or, 'when I'm in a deep mood'). Apart from the children, not one of them has gone to school.

They have an old gramophone and go for popular African jazz records, whose repetitive rhythms echo the monotonies of their life. No garden, no pets, no fancy stuff. But as Simon works at a bakery, he is sometimes given cakes and confectionery.

The variations are near-infinite, but somewhere in this picture, every mother's son and daughter of you will find himself.

Your varied reactions have confused many people. Your problem is simple: so much to pay for, yet so very much less to earn. Economic facts are hard, they tell us, so some way you've got to square the arithmetical difference that decides between your happiness and misery. Almost everywhere you have turned to extra activities. Part-time work such as selling soft goods, night-time sewing, kids caddying at golf courses, or carrying packets at market places.

Or *Nyanyatha*, which includes the range from pick-pocketing and handbag-snatching to burglary and robbery. But this is not really you, the criminal, the delinquent tsotsi.

More like you is the concerned animal who consents to let your children bring home, nights, mysterious bales of stuff about which questions are not asked. Or you, when you accept the purchase of goods at the back-door — at half-price when you know darned well they were not obtained from the legal train.

It's not even you when, dead-tired and harried to

madness by creditors, you have no time or energy left
to worry about where your teenage son — or worse —
teenage daughter is at 12 o'clock at night.

Trapped, concerned, dazed by the screaming
demands of your budget, you gape and groan. There
must be a better way for humans to live than this.

WORLD'S LONGEST WALK TO WORK!

Azikhwelwa! For all its fierce passion and aggressive power this slogan of the bus boycott in Johannesburg and Pretoria is in the passive voice. No-one uses the active voice forms of 'ningasikhweli!' (Don't board them) and 'angizikhweli!' (I don't board them). The passive voice form expresses the mute long-suffering and frustration of a voiceless people. But more, much more. It is the cry of the caged animal trying to find a way out. The little hiss through the tiny puncture in the high-pressured world.

The bus firm, Putco, had a case. Increased running costs, increased wages, had made it impossible for it to continue operating the bus systems without increasing fares.

Then suddenly January 7 was upon us. The day of the increased fares. And the boycott was on. Grim-faced people walked the nine miles to work and the nine miles back to their homes in Alexandra. Sophia-towners walked gaily, chattily. Then there was a meeting in the evening. This was not so much a meeting to consolidate the boycott as to discuss what to do about the taxis who charged 2s to town. Some

taximen suggested they might consider reducing to
1s 6d. Some people yelled, 'What, one-and-six! We
want fourpence, man!' The taxis appealed, and the
deal was settled at 1s.

Then commerce, industry and the City Council got
worried. But nothing could really be done until the
Minister of Transport, Mr B J Schoeman, returned
from abroad. And when he did return, the first
utterance on the boycott issue was that it should be
broken: the ANC was testing its strength: people who
gave lifts to boycotters were misguided; bosses should
cut the pay of workers who came late. But the
boycott went on. On and on, on foot, on bicycles, on
horse-drawn carts, in taxis, in cars of sympathisers, in
vans, in lorries. The police were here, were there,
were everywhere. First the police stopped the cars of
lift-givers, and there were many allegations of threats
of arrest, and suggestions that lift-giving was illegal.
The people protested. Then the police hauled out the
Africans and arrested those who did not have passes
or tax receipts. Pirate taxis were swept off the map.
But the people walked on at 500 miles a month.

The City Council of Johannesburg, the Chamber of
Commerce and the Chamber of Industry came
together to see what to do. They appealed to the
boycotters to cut it out. They were laughed at.
Members of the Non-European Affairs Department
met anonymous African leaders in secret to find a way
out. Then came the abortive beerhall boycott —
just because someone had suggested that Putco could
be subsidised from the Native Services Levy Fund,
which is financed by beerhall profits. But the people
loved their beer too much!

Then there was talk, in this atmosphere of shooting
off your mouth, of boycotting trains because the

Government was using them to break the boycott,
and the boycotting of White shops because (I think)
there was so little vocal White sympathy for the
troubles of the African. What was actually happening
was that the African (with all other Non-Europeans
looking on) was indeed discovering that he has a way
to make himself heard. This boycott which I have
pursued, started so innocently, which was almost
thrust upon me in my economic lot by the gods,
has shown me a weapon I have not until now dreamt
of! That is what the boycott has become. A terrific
eye-opener, especially now that the Government has
chosen to look upon it as a challenge, 'the showdown'.
But the way to it has been accidental: it has been by
way of getting tired of being pushed around, and
getting used to seeing police guns pushed in your
face. That spark of hope, of strength, is the true cause,
lying underneath the implacable spirit of Alexandra
the Great! The boycott has been 100 per cent successful as is the spirit it engenders. Boycotters who say,
'You separate us further away from our work, and
then you expect us to pay more for transport,' are
people who have seen the boycott as a weapon for
the future.

The boycotters walked on. They slogged up the
hills. They slushed through the rain. They shouted,
'Azikhwelwa!' (The buses shall not be boarded). Then
came the sympathy boycotts as the movement
spread. Moroka with no fare increase at all went on
boycott in sympathy with the people of Alexandra
and Sophiatown. This they did in the teeth of
Advisory Board opposition. George Goch and Randfontein joined in. They did not even have Putco
buses. So everybody wrangled and nothing was being
done to bring the boycott to an end. Commerce met,

but would not discuss wage increases. Check! The
people met, but would not give up the boycott.
Check! The police came, but could not break the
boycott. Check! The matter was discussed in Parlia-
ment, but the Government would not give way no
matter whether the boycott lasted a month or six
months. Stalemate!

GIRLS IN HIGH-HEEL SHOES

The Modern African Miss. She's city-slick and sophisticated. She's smart. She's delicate and unselfcon-
scious in the way she handles men, the home and life.
And that's been achieved in less than fifty years, for
fifty years ago she was content to sit in the sunshine
of mud walls and on dung-smeared floors.

And, because of new jobs — not just kitchen chores
— jobs in the factories, in department stores, clerical
jobs, secretarial jobs, social welfare jobs, nursing jobs,
teaching jobs, the Modern Miss has got her red-
painted talons on to more money than she has seen
before.

More money has meant a more elegant way of
living. At first she was gaudy and brash, and flourished
her newly-won freedom and funds in the colourful
manner of the prostitute and brazen flirt. Grey old
heads shook themselves sadly.

But soon she learned grace and poise and finesse.
True, this brought brand-new problems for her man.
This creature was talking back, was catty and gossipy
was asking for nylon stockings, was going to 'nice-
time parties' at holy hours of the night and returning

at unholy hours of the day, good heavens! She was even reading disturbing books!

Even the domestic servant was speaking English with an un-African accent which I can only blame her mistress for. But she was a lovely dream. In the home she looked like the delightful things that they put in magazines. And when one's educated friends were present, she could hold her own in the conversation, argument and dignity. You sat back and looked in wonder at this woman, not long out of the loin-cloth, now draped in python gowns and making her point with a long cigarette holder.

True again, she now talks about those unheard of things: divorce, abortion, feminine rights, and mere males. But, well understood and treated square, she's a lovely feline, stimulating to the mind, satisfying to the creature desires, at once an ornament and an ordeal. Some people hazard marriage with them, then grin and bear it. Others just have their fling with them.

And she's a woman of the world. Whereas in the days gone by she didn't think much beyond the kraal walls, she now imagines herself as a Lena Horne, a Vijayalakshmi Pandit, or a Madame Chiang Kai-Shek. Only thirty years ago she never thought of marrying anybody outside her tribe, now she writes romantic pen-pal letters to men in Ghana and Nigeria.

Perhaps the crassness and immaturity that inevitably goes with swift development brought a knotty crudeness to the way women adapted themselves to the new situation. But they're arriving in style. To us men it means a new attitude, a new factor in our calculation of the problem of the black man and himself.

But we're not going to make it sociological. We're

going to grin at the tricky packet of femininity, while we try to solve it. But we realise that the Modern Miss is catching up with modern times and with us. God save us when she by-passes us, like the American woman has by-passed her man.

But nevertheless I thank the Bigshot for bringing her in line with modern times and fashions. The other day I went to Mapokkerstad, about 35 miles north of Pretoria. The village was lovely with the houses painted in varying colours, styles and designs. The women there went in for natural beauty, with frank breasts jutting out like promontories. It was very romantic, just the sedative for jaded, city nerves.

But the thought came to me that the shattering silence would get me down, and I would panic back to the near-thing life of Sophiatown and some loud-mouthed, bewitching girl. The wonderful girl of my dreams.

RUSSIAN FAMO SESH!

A dark figure swathed in a coloured blanket swerved from the muddy pavement into the dark yard of a house. Soon similar figures appeared, men and women, the men looking ferocious and carrying sticks, the women lascivious with blue artificial pimples or 'beauty' lines painted on their faces. Now and then a giggle would come from the dark, and straining eyes would discern two dark forms clinging to each other. From the house came the music of an organ, harmonicas, the shrieking of voices, the stomping of feet. That is Famo, the famous sex dance of the Russians, Basotho gangsters of the Reef. The place was Germiston Location.

We slid out of the car and went in. It was a stunning scene, so cramped with swarming life and sweating bodies. There were long wooden benches along the walls, and Russian men and women had filled them in the order of man and woman, man and woman, man and woman right round the room. In the centre were sweating dancers yelling their heads and the roof off.

The men just swayed. The women were the stars. They danced a primitive thing that looked strangely

like jive. Now and again, at little climaxes in the song
and the dance, the women kicked up their legs to
show panties, and with some of them, no panties. The
men ogled and goggled.

But in their ogling and goggling they were secretly
choosing the women who seemed to promise them
most. There was liquor, too, mostly KB. Then in
bustled mine hostess. She was a short Mosotho
woman, nicely stacked, beaming hospitality now,
bristling hostility a moment after. As she approached
us I saw she carried a gourd of beer. She did a
prancing dance in front of us and yelled, 'Eu! Eu! Eu!
Eu! Eu!' She thrust the gourd at me, and to show my
manliness I took a big, long swig.

Suddenly commotion broke loose in one corner.
Men with raised sticks rushed at a young man with a
girl on his lap. It looked like murder. I went close to
find out what it was all about. Everybody was jabbering. I waited for a forest of sticks to rain down
on the young man, and they were poised in the air
like the spears of a barbarian horde.

Manyeyu, mine hostess, shouted above the din:
'*Khele, le sele!*' (Hell, but you people are naughty!)
Everybody laughed and sticks came down slowly. It
was all a rough joke. I wiped the sweat off my brow.

The organ went groaning again, harmonicas wailed,
human voices took up the lament and the crowd
started dancing. I watched a young woman near me.
She was dancing a dance all on her own. She stood in
one spot, but her body was darting back and forth
like a cobra preparing for an attack. Suddenly she
kicked up her leg. A flash of petticoat, a dash of
panties. Not content with that attack on my modesty,
she whirled round, stopped before me, and yanked
her dress up over her head in a swift movement so

that I saw knees, thighs, black panties, belly and a navel. She threw out a leg clean over my head. I bought more hooch.

As the night wore on I noticed that the crowd was thinning. I went out of the stuffy room into the night air. I noticed that some of the girls who had been dancing were walking off arm in arm with blanket-robed Russian men. I went to the yard. I hurried back. I had seen enough. In the open couples were making love.

BOOZERS BEWARE OF BARBERTON!

Number 17, Marshall Street, Ferreirastown, Johannesburg, is just about the craziest address I've met. So many people who have lived there have gone mad, even as so many other people have stood in the slummy yard drinking that poisonous brew of shebeen invention — barberton. There is an obvious connection. But the startling fact is that four of these people lived and went mad in the same room.

A South African neurologist has just sent a paper to America on barberton. He has found that it does drive certain people mad.

In the Forties, they say, a coloured woman living in this yard and selling barberton thought that her neighbours might want to take away her profitable trade in shebeen liquor. So in the dead of night she decided to 'put the jinx' on this room, and here and there in the yard, by planting magic. Not long after this people began to behave strangely.

That's their story of how it all started, but the facts of what happened subsequently is hardly less startling. At about this time there lived in the fatal room, Chris Tyssen, his wife, and Willem Tyssen, his brother. Chris suddenly found out that his wife was unhappy with him. They were always quarrelling and fighting, until one day she just deserted him to go and live in Pretoria. This affected Chris so badly that he became very ill, and sometimes would mutter delirious nonsense. Then suddenly his brother, Willem, started to act crazy. This was more serious than Chris's condition which was described as having had 'just a touch'. Willem did mad things like collecting bits of paper, old tins, rubbish. Then he vanished. People looked for him everywhere. Not a sign of him. Not a sound about him, for over two months. Then came the rumour that an unidentified body had been found in Germiston. He had been drowned in a lake there. The police did not suspect foul play, but his friends are still uneasy. He was given a pauper's funeral.

Chris was ejected from the room, but he still stays in the yard, sleeping outside on a miserable mattress with the stars for a blanket. He wanders in and out like a lost, bewildered animal.

But just opposite this notorious room is the Fourie room. Here lived Willie 'Oom Johnnie ' Fourie and his wife, Maria. Unlike many of the other victims, Oom Johnnie did not get ill at all. He was completely healthy on the night of March 17, 1957, when he suddenly got it into his head that he wanted to make a great speech. He stripped himself stark naked, grabbed an axe and jumped on to the table to deliver his great oration. He made a magnificent figure standing there in his innocence and the light casting an enormous, distorted shadow on the wall and roof.

The people rushed out and sent for the Flying Squad. He was removed from there and taken to the 'mad cells' at Newlands Police Station where he was

duly garbed in a blanket and left among the other
mixed-ups. His wife, Maria, went to see him on the
following Thursday. He seemed all right. But when
she went to see him again, she heard that he had died.

'*Those whom the gods wish to destroy, they first
make mad.*'

The wife is so distracted by the death of Oom
Johnnie, that she's a thin edge away herself from
daylight clear levelheadedness. She moves about in a
daze and mumbles, 'Me, I don't want to talk. I don't
want to talk. I don't want to talk.'

But the yard in which she lives has become the
talk of Malay Camp (Ferreirastown). And in that
Doom Room, now occupied by two brothers, it looks
like violence plans to strike again. These two brothers
are very fond of each other. The other day they had
been having a brotherly drink together and got a
little high. When they got home the elder brother just
suddenly attacked his kid brother. They had a wild
fight, throwing in everything they could lay their
hands on, kicking, biting, fisting. They smashed
two of the large window-panes of the Doom Room.
The following day when I got there they had con-
tracted a sulky truce, and it was obvious there was
no longer so much bad blood between them. But the
people in the yard intimated to me in hushed whispers
that they knew it was the jinx over the room striking
again.

I think, however, there is a much simpler explanation of the phenomenon. Next to Maria Fourie's
room there's another room whose role in this business
is much more ominous than people realise. This is the
house where they sell barberton in a big way. African
men come from the neighbouring mines, the town,
and industrial concerns for their mugful of *mbamba*

(barberton). But barberton is a poison made in such a way as to give a quick kick. It is made of bread, yeast and sugar. Its main characteristic is that it is 'raw' (swiftly prepared) liquor. One of its commonest effects is against the skin which peels off and sallows. People get red lips and purulent black pimples on the face. But it has made those who have drunk it for a long time raging madmen, especially in fights. Here then may lie the answer to the mystery of the yard of lunatics. That the people have fed too long and too much on a poisonous concoction. It has made them sick and driven them mad.

OUR HUNGRY CHILDREN

It has now come to be called 'The Story of a Boy called Simon'. That is because of James Ambrose Brown's sensitive article in the *Sunday Times* ('I Think Aloud', the column is called, but it has got people to scream aloud). The article described the pathetic condition of our schoolchildren who come to classes hungry and can think only of food.

The great rewarding thing about that article is that it has roused the conscience of South Africans. For after the *Sunday Times* had published it, 'thousands answered the cry of the schoolchildren.' It will need many more than those thousands, however, before more than a fraction of our children get their breakfast.

The position is that there is an African Children's Feeding Scheme run by a group of very active men and women. Their great nightmare is that they don't have enough funds to feed all the children. A few years ago the Government contributed 2d per child for the working of this scheme. Later, as the result of official policy that 'Africans should be made to pay for their own development', this government contribution was cut to 1½d.

At the time there were muffled outcries of 'Shame!' and 'The people who can least afford to pay are being given less.' But the protests spluttered out.

Then two years ago, the Government put a tricky question to African parents: Choose, which would you rather have, expansion of African education — or school-feeding? Knowledge — or food?

It was a bitter choice, but the people decided in favour of school expansion, and the 1½d trickle dried up.

The other day I went to a school in Orlando, Johannesburg, to see how the children get along, whether they have breakfast or how they manage without it. The first classroom wasn't a classroom. The children — aged seven, six, eight — just sat on long benches alongside a school building in the winter sun. I needn't have asked the questions I asked for, merely by looking at their ash-grey lips and listless manner, I should have known that these children had had precious little to eat that morning. And I could see that some of them just didn't have the strength to gaily join in that adventure of youth — the process of education. There were about 25 in that class.

'How many of you had nothing to eat this morning?' I asked. Twelve small hands went up. One small fellow, tremblingly told me that there had been a crust of bead at home that morning, and he had brought it to eat during 'play-time'.

He looked up at me, and I had some fleeting vision of an English workhouse boy asking for more.

A few little girls told me that they had left home without anything to eat — not even water, which was too cold in the morning. One boy, with a battered khaki tunic for a coat, said that it was not always that he didn't eat, but that morning 'there was nothing'. Some mornings he did manage to get black tea, sometimes with a little sugar.

Another group in this class had only tea. Then there was the group that had had tea with a slice of dry bread. In this particular class there was not one that had had soft porridge, but quite a few had been given a cold slice from last night's mealie pap.

Through all the classes I visited, the story was monotonously the same. Here and there I found evidence of children who had come from the 'better-off' homes. In one Standard Six class I found a boy, about 16, who got 10s a day pocket-money from his shopkeeper-father. But most of them come to school with fortunes ranging from 1d to 3d.

This they spend on fat cakes and polony from a nearby café. This café also serves soup, that tasted fairly nourishing to me, at 2d a plate. Even at 2d, very few children can afford the soup.

In the same class I found two girls who complained that they often have spells of dizziness because of hunger, and find it hard to concentrate. A teacher told me that she has had to adjust her time-table so that 'hard-head' subjects, like arithmetic, are done early, before pupils can realise how hungry they are.

When I trod through the classrooms and watched those children wrestling with bad odds against a tough environment, it occurred to me that this was just one end of the story — the end where the children at least looked washed and gym-dressed. I sought to go and visit the homes from which some of them came.

Early one morning I went to the home of seven-year-old Patience Bothile, in Orlando East. I caught her just as she was getting up, preparing for the day, a bitterly cold one. She was in a flannel petticoat. She slipped on a flimsy dress and carried a little bath tub to the tap attached to the lavatory. She got cold water and started to wash.

Inside the kitchen was a stove fire, and nearby two young boys were tinkering with a pressure stove, which flared and faded now and then. It was obvious that there wouldn't be tea for little Patience.

By now she was shivering, blowing her warm breath into her cupped hands. She got into her smart gym dress, white shirt, and battered shoes. She took her school case, and, with all the patience in the world, ran off to school.

She has a sweet face, dulled by the cold and the hunger fluttering inside her. I knew what just a cup of hot broth, a slice of bread with peanut butter could do for this dear child. I'm told it would cost just a tickey. Somebody's got to find that blasted tickey!

NUDE PASS PARADE

Naked. Humiliated. Hoping to God time's going to go quickly. Trying to pass off awkwardness with a shrug and wry jokes, big-shot businessmen, professional men, ordinary guys just come for a 'pass' stand around stripped in the waiting-room of the Non-European Affairs Department in Johannesburg each work-day of the week. Hundreds of them, each day.

You want a 'pass'. Right. You go into a structure that looks like a public convenience. It is on the corner of Albert and Polly Streets in Johannesburg. You find a 'blackjack' — one of those black-uniformed municipal policemen — sitting on a high stool. He barks at you that you should not be an idiot: can't you join the queue! You join the queue of hundreds of other Africans, and you get counted off.

If you are in the batch that is to see the doctor for a medical certificate you get a little ticket that permits you to enter the eastern gate to the great building of the city's Non-European Affairs Department. You join another queue that goes in and out of iron railings and right into the building.

Inside you meet white-coated clerks and medical

aides who yell you into removing your top clothing, yell you into joining a queue that leads to a green curtained room, and yell others off from this sacrosanct queue.

In due course you get your turn to step up to the X-ray machine, hug it according to instructions, and your chest gets X-rayed. Then you pass into an inner room where you are curtly told to drop your trousers, all of you in a row.

You may be a dignified businessman, a top-class lawyer, a jeweller, a wood merchant, or anybody. You will find yourself naked. Well, you wanted a permit to work in Johannesburg, didn't you? The official world is not finicky about your embarrassed modesty.

Recently the Non-European Affairs Department issued a new instruction that all Africans who work for themselves, that is, all Africans who don't work for a European, must also be registered. This edict affects some of the élite members of African society: businessmen, doctors, musicians, lawyers and also those who are still looking for work.

There seems to be an obvious connection with the panic over the Reef's crime wave, for many people have blamed the workless Africans for the crimes, and some of the businessmen are blamed for encouraging thefts and robberies by receiving stolen goods.

Mr John Raditsebe, of 71 Victoria Road, Sophiatown, Johannesburg, is a watchmaker. He has a little shop near the corner of Ray Street. Behind his shop are living quarters. Sometimes he has to work deep into the night to cope with the demand for his services.

Like so many others he had to go fix his 'passes'. He too, had to walk the gauntlet of humiliation. 'This pass, however,' he says, 'is so precious that one shuts one's eyes and goes through with the miserable experience.'

Then there's Mr W Lubengu, also of Sophiatown, a wood merchant. Mr Rufus Khoza, of the famous Manhattan Brothers, now a world-famous singer. And more and more.

One of the most startling things that has come from this strange business is the verdict of the people affected themselves. Terse, tired. 'Official contempt!' That is all they say.

The authorities claim that the humiliation of the mass naked parade is unavoidable. If they tried to give everyone individual attention they wouldn't have time to get through their work, they say.

Pressed further, one official said: 'What's so wrong with this, after all. Why, during the war, old men, young men had to strip all together. They thought nothing of it.'

But, Mr Official, Mr Non-European Affairs Department, Mr Everybody who thinks things like these are all right: We aren't at war. There's no emergency. We're a civilised country, we keep telling the rest of the world.

ZEERUST: WHAT THE MEN SAY ABOUT IT

Another girl, young and cocky — she might have been one of the domestic servants in Johannesburg's suburbs — hugged her hands into her half-white apron over her breasts, and spat at me a tirade: 'What war is this that fights women? What law is this when our chief who is not our chief, and his beat-up men, have no more respect for the huts of their fellow-men and beat up their women.

'It must be a difficult law that cannot be explained but by sticks and stones, and our own men cannot come from Kgotla feeling our customs still work. I know, I know, because my uncle often came home at night and all he could say was that the times are tarnished . . . *dinako dimaswe*.

'I will never carry a pass. That is why I am here now, but my heart is crying for our lands that go dead and our cattle that are wandering in the bush.'

A haggard old lady, leaning heavily on a snake-like stick, and Time's inroads heavily etched on her face, spoke tremblingly. One would have thought that she had reached that stage in life where she would have resigned herself to all. But she said her say: 'Rather

would we let the tribe perish than accept these passes.
We are Bafurutse who lived in the land of our forefathers, but this side of the mountain (she meant the
border) there are Bafurutse too.

'You must hear me well, my son, do you hear me?
We are not law-breakers, but people with broken
heads who have fled to safety, to people of our
people whose hearts have not yet been poisoned.

'If we can know that back home we may return
without the beating of women, the stoning of small
children and the burning of houses we would return
now. There is where we have our loved ones and our
possessions.'

Her trembling voice made many of the men look
down or away.

I felt that not here were any of the people who
supported the passes for women. Those must still be
back there in the villages where the chiefs' guardsmen
enforced compliance with the law. I'd have liked to
talk to some of them, to listen as freely as to these.
But there was the regulation about entering the reserve.

I tried to explain that the Government might say
that there would never have been any trouble if, like
good tribesmen, they had obeyed the law and taken
the passes. If the people had shown the age-old
respect for their chiefs. If the people had not listened
to dangerous advice.

There followed a heated argument that I was there
to try them, to find blame with them. But one
wizened man explained that 'the things this young
man has mentioned' must be answered. He took it
upon himself.

Carefully he went over old ground explaining to
me that before the passes came there had been no
trouble. The chief didn't feel forced to carry out

unpopular laws without the support of the Kgotla. There was no need for policemen around.

Then came the passes, and the women said, 'No', and their men said, 'No'. Then the police came, and then came the trouble.

'When we couldn't stand it any more we ran into Bechuanaland. Do you see now?'

On the whole the men refugees in Bechuanaland, sympathetic to the women's resistance to the passes, were, however, more concerned with the break-up of the tribe, tribal institutions, and the waste of their lands and the neglect of their cattle.

A few of the refugees were bitter about the stand that some of their chiefs had taken on the side of the Government. Others resented mainly the attacks alleged to have been made on their wives and children.

One pungently declared: 'If my wife no more belongs to me, let the Government pay me back my lobola and have her.'

The sun was softly flushing the western sky with its gold when I closed the meeting with the words, *'Pula! Pula!'* (Rain! Rain!).

These refugees live in crude huts, not unlike those they occupied in the Union, but few have any means of livelihood or any confidence in the future. Most of them don't have any work, but at least the chiefs there are trying to find pieces of land for them.

A day or two after my 'Press conference', I went to see the gate of escape — the entrance into Bechuanaland from the Union. It is just about four miles from Lobatsi. A simple white structure, ten yards from where the fence was cut and with a white pole-boom barring the way. The place is guarded by armed Bechuanaland police.

Once, I was told, the Union police were hot on the heels of a fleeing refugee who just managed to duck under the white pole into Bechuanaland. They stood there, helplessly watching their quarry's escape.

One of the chiefs pleaded with the refugee from the Union side of the border, telling him to come back to his motherland, that he would be forgiven and treated well, that his farm and cattle would be saved. The young man waved a stubborn goodbye, and disappeared round a bend.

Another border anecdote tells of the Union police arriving, panting heavily, at the 'white pole'. They pleaded with the border patrol to allow them only a few hours inside Bechuanaland so that they might retrieve the Union's nationals. After long argument, the Union police were told that they might enter, provided that they left their firearms at the border. The Union police thought that it was not worth the trouble, the anecdote goes.

The greatest concentration of refugees is at Ramoutsa, where a young enlightened chief is deeply concerned about their welfare. There are about 720 of them, and every day more and more are dodging in.

Chief Kgosi is all the time allocating plots to them, and by all signs they will be the soonest assimilated.

One of the Ramoutsa refugees has had quite a time. In the clashes at Gopanestad his father got hurt and had to be removed to a Johannesburg hospital. His mother also received severe injuries and was taken to the Zeerust Hospital. His elder brother, who was studying at a university, had to abandon his studies and come home, only to find that life there was too dangerous. So he ducked into Bechuanaland.

The younger brother lives a Robin Hood kind of

life, slipping into the Union at night to go and see his family, and slipping back in the early hours of the morning.

Meanwhile there are many refugees scattered all over Bechuanaland. The local chiefs try their best to place them, but in most places they cannot concentrate them in homogeneous groups.

At Mochudi in the middle of the night I saw two vans loaded with young refugees, brown naked bodies looking anxiously this way and that.

I was told that they were the latest arrivals, and that the vans were taking them to various places where the chief had found sleeping place for them for that night.

Only at Mahalapye did I find one man, Theophilus Tomocha, who thought and said that the refugees could fry in their own stew for all he cared. Why don't they return to the Union and settle the dispute with their own government? he said.

Maybe the bitterness will burn out of the hearts of the refugees. Maybe, more than sanctuary, they will find a home and a patriotism in Bechuanaland.

Perhaps in that country, promising to become an important mining territory, they will be able to contribute towards prosperity and share in it one day.

But they will find it hard ever to look back at the Union kindly and without sadness, if one is to judge by what they are saying.

DINOKANA, THE TARGET!

Tribal areas are under fire. The Bantu Authorities Act and the question of passes for women have attacked various villages and tribes in the country. Now it is Dinokana, in the Zeerust district. 1. The chief has been deposed. 2. Passes have been issued to women and have been refused and burned. 3. The modern primary school has been boycotted and the boycotting children will never again attend school in the Union. 4. Houses of suspect tribesmen have been burnt, including that of the principal of the school. 5. A white shopkeeper's business has been boycotted. 6. Scores of people have been arrested on various charges. 7. The tramp, tramp, tramp of police marches into Dinokana. It has driven the people to fear, and to anger. And that fear and anger has spread to other nearby districts: Gopane, Motswedi, Shupingstad, Braklaagte, Haartebeesfontein, Leeuwfontein, Stryfontein . . . all shuddering villages.

But it is a long story. In 1952 eight tribesmen complained to the Native Commissioner, Mr Hattingh, that they had had difficulty in meeting the chief, Abraham Moiloa, in order to discuss with him what

they considered to be his laxity about tribal administration. They were requesting the Native Commissioner to use his influence to persuade the chief to
meet them. The then Commissioner asked them to
send him a letter about their complaints. They did so
but heard nothing of the affair after that. The tribe
continued its somnolent life.

Four years later, in October, 1956, the new Commissioner, C R Richter, came across this 1952 letter
of complaint from the eight tribesmen. He called for
an enquiry under Commissioner Holt from Pilanesberg
to investigate the complaints. The chief's uncle, Boaz
Moiloa, refused to testify against the chief.

At this enquiry one tribesman told the Com-
missioners: 'You antagonise the chief and the tribe,
the chief and the Government, the tribe and the
Government. The chief is the wife of the tribe. You
can't try him at a Native Commissioner's court. Try
him before the tribe at Kgotla. He is called Mmabatho
(Mother of the people).' This was in September 1956.

But this year, on March 29, the chief was ordered
by Commissioner Richter to instruct the women to
accept reference books. The chief was opposed to this
move. On March 31, Chief Abraham Moiloa told a
meeting of the women that he had been instructed by
the authorities to order the women in his tribe to
fetch their reference books.

Meanwhile on April 2 the chief was instructed to
call a Kgotla for the 4th. At the meeting of the 4th
appeared the Commissioner, Richter, and Holtz-
hausen, the Chief Native Commissioner from Potchef-
stroom. Even before the meeting got underway, the
Chief Native Commissioner summarily told Chief
Abraham Moiloa to get out of the chief's chair for
he was no longer chief. Just like that. No notice of

deposition. No prior warning. No opportunity to state his case. He was given 14 days to leave for Ventersdorp or Vryburg.

Bafurutse tribesmen working in Johannesburg came to Dinokana in Putco buses to consider the happenings at home. Some of them may have been members of the African National Congress, but they all regarded themselves as Bafurutse individuals — 'Sons of Dinokana' — and it was to the Bafurutse call that they were responding. Then the fireworks! On April 13, some women went round and collected reference books from the seventy odd who had taken them, and in the dark of night they burned them in a bonfire. Some of the people called an unofficial 'court' to try those considered as having caused the deposition of the chief. Four of these men, it was alleged in the offficial court later, were then dragged to this 'court' and tried as being traitors to the tribe and informers to the Government.

These four men were: Michael Moiloa Johannes Moiloa, Lavius Kebine and Modiri Moiloa. It is alleged by the Crown that they were found guilty by the so-called 'court' and sentenced to death. They were to be hurled down the ancient Mamokoti pit. In olden days this pit was used as a place of execution for witches and traitors. The four victims were alleged to have been tied by the hands and led off to a bone-shattering death. They were saved by the wailing of the women and the timely arrival of the police, it is alleged.

When the police came they found a mob in a threatening mood. They retreated, until reinforcements came from Rustenburg. Then followed house-burning and witch-hunting.

Johannes Moiloa, married to Nkutu, sister of Chief

Abraham Moiloa, is one of the most frightened men in Zeerust. He fears for his life. His house in Dinokana has been burned down. He has gone to live in Mafeking, but had to come to Zeerust to give evidence in a case of incitement to murder.

Then there is the case of the principal of the primary school in Dinokana. He supported the move for reference books for women. The people went mad. They thought that he was in cahoots with the police and the Commissioner. So they burned down his house, and organised a boycott of the school. Only 146 out of 1 200 attended on the first day of the boycott. The school principal contacted the Commissioner who relayed the matter to the authorities in Pretoria.

The following afternoon Pretoria ordered that the school should be closed down on the current roll, that the teachers should be transferred, and that the names of the boycotting children should be taken down and circularised — so that they will not be allowed to receive education in the Union for the rest of their lives.

The big boys in Pretoria took a serious attitude to these happenings, and organised a special riot squad of police under Sergeant Van Rooyen to tackle the situation in the area.

Boaz Moiloa, uncle of the chief, has been offered chieftainship by the authorities. He has refused. 1. He will not take over the chieftainship when the rightful chief is still alive. 2. He will not take over the chieftainship without the consent of the tribe expressed at a legal Kgotla, and a legal Kgotla can only be called by the rightful chief. 3. He fears that if he accepts chieftainship the suspicion will be on him that he had a part in arranging the deposition of the chief.

During one of the many visits of the police to Dinokana, the people were told: 'Remember the monument!' This referred to a heap of stones in Dinokana. In the 1850s the Bafurutse prepared to resist the Boers of Zeerust by fighting. They were overcome. Then an agreement was made with Paul Kruger to the effect that the Bafurutse should never fight the Boers and the land where they stayed — Dinokana (Many Streams) — would forever be theirs. The 'monument' was intended to remind the Bafurutse about this agreement.

Because the tribesmen think that a white trader, Callaghan, supports passes for women, they boycotted him as soon as trouble began. They took their custom to an Indian, Reheman who made a roaring trade, but phtt! down came the official hand on him. He has been given three months to quit Dinokana for he is regarded as an 'agitator'. Reheman claims that he is completely innocent of politics.

He has grown up and lived as a Bafurutse. He speaks their language even in his own home. He has 'gone African' and probably has some sympathy for the tribesmen. But as for politics, nothing!

A similar thing happened to another Indian trader in Gopane. When the trouble over the reference books shifted to Gopane, he was given notice to quit. The reason given was that the authorities wanted to start implementing the Tomlinson Report.

What is happening in all these places, Witzieshoek, Sekhukhuniland, Zululand, Dinokana, is that the application of the Bantu Authorities Act is destroying the very thing it purports to set up — Bantu Authorities. What the authorities want is not Bantu chiefs with their own power to rule their tribes according to ancient tribal customs and tradition. They want officials to carry out their policies, like passes for women.

Dinokana is now a grim, unhappy place. I think there is something boiling underneath its depressing quiet. I think the young men are planning an explosion. But the air is heavy with menace and the only really cheerful voice came from a little child. As we drove out of Dinokana, she shouted 'Ta, ta!' I wondered to how many old, revered treasures of Dinokana that 'ta, ta' meant 'Goodbye!'

LET THE PEOPLE DRINK

I went to a little one-room apartment in Good Street, Sophiatown, Johannesburg. It is perched in the sky like a dove-cote, and you have to go up a flight of rickety steps to get there. There was a door like a shed door. I knocked and called: 'Ousie! Ousie!' A bolt screeched back, and a broad face peered at me. Then the door opened, and I stepped into a shabby passage.

I was led to a second door beyond which I heard the drone of voices. I walked into a very well furnished, brightly lit room. Modern jazz music of the hotttest kind blared at me. And the room was crowded with African men and women sitting in clusters of threes and fours, enjoying — most of them — beer. The amber quart bottles stood all over, full, half-full, and empty. But here and there a party was drinking brandy from tumblers measured accurately to the fourth finger.

This was the famous 'Little Heaven', Sophiatown's poshest shebeen.

'Hi, Can!' called the huge hostess, 'what evil plans bring you here?' Then she turned to the house at

large, and announced: 'Say, folks, Can here is Mr
DRUM. Maybe you'll soon find yourself in DRUM.'

I grinned pointlessly. I had to, because I recognised
a couple of fellows who belonged to Sophiatown's
toughest gang. I didn't want them to think I was
doing a story on them.

'Well, Can, what can we do for you?' asked the
hostess.

'Beer,' I said.

'I got whisky, you know.'

'Yes, but beer,' I insisted.

I sat down on the studio couch, and looked around.
In a corner on the bed I saw three very respectable
people, two men and a woman, sipping quietly from
their glasses. The woman was a very well known staff
nurse. She caught my eye and smiled sweetly. The
men turned round, and I recognised two teachers
from one of Sophiatown's primary schools.

My drink came.

Half-way down my quart of beer, an African
constable, cloaked in a heavy khaki green overcoat
entered. Another one without an overcoat followed
close upon his heels. They joined me on the studio
couch, and I could see sergeant's stripes on the arm of
the one without an overcoat.

Nobody turned a hair. The fellows at the table
didn't even break their argument over the Freedom
Charter. Our hostess waddled up to the cops. They
ordered half-a-jack of brandy. And they paid for it!

I rose quietly, and went to say goodbye to the
hostess. I still had quite a few shebeens to visit that
night, and many nights after.

In my ramblings round the shebeens of Johannesburg, I found that they were not all as comfortable
and cheerful and 'safe' as 'Little Heaven'.

Those in the townships are of two kinds. There are
the handsome, respectable ones like Little Heaven
and The Sanctuary in Sophiatown, The Greenhouse
in Newclare, The Kind Lady and The Gardens in
Western Township, The Basement in Orlando, and
Paradise in George Goch. These make you feel at
home, and the atmosphere is friendly and sociable.
There are kids to go and buy soda water, ginger ale,
or Indian tonic for you. There is often a private room
where you can 'sleep it off' if you've had too many.
These shebeens have obviously ploughed some of
their profits into the business.

But there are those that are just out to make money,
and damn the customer. They are dirty, and crowded,
and hostile. The shebeen queen is always hurrying
you to drink quickly, and swearing at somebody or
other. 'You b—s act as if you've licences to drink!'
She sells everything, brandy, gin, beer and skokiaan,
hops, hoenene, barberton, pineapple, and even more
violent concoctions. It is in these that 'doping' takes
place.

'Doping' is the weakening or fortifying of the
strength of brandy and gin. These drinks are so
precious, expensive, and difficult to come by that
these shebeen queens often 'dope' them with water,
or black tea, or even tobacco water, to increase the
amount, or to give them a quick kick.

The prices in the shebeens vary. A quart of beer
may cost 3/6 to 6/-. A 'straight' of brandy or gin,
between 14/6 and 26/-. A bottle of whisky, between
30/- and 50/-. At one Syrian shebeen in Ferreirastown,
you pay 14/6 for a bottle of brandy if you take it
away and 20/- if you have it there. It is safer for the
'house' if you take it right away with you. Quite
often you may get liquor below retail prices. This is

because it has been stolen from a bottle store, and the whole price is sheer profit.

But I wanted to find out where all this liquor comes from. This was tough because nobody wants to talk. Not only from fear of the police, but because shebeens don't want to give away their 'holes' — the sources of their supplies.

My break came when a friend of mine arranged that I be taken along when the 'boys' made a trip to go and fetch supplies for the weekend. We met in town on the corner of Diagonal and Sauer Streets. A grey van picked us up. I sat in front with the driver and my friend, and as I looked back over my shoulder, I saw two other chaps, unknown to me, sitting in the van. Beyond them covering the door of the van at the back was a lot of flowers, placed so that you could not see into the van when the door was open.

Nobody would tell me exactly where we were going. We travelled through byways and back streets for about a half an hour, when we came to what appeared to be the outskirts of a town. From the registration numbers of the cars I saw, I knew that we were near Vereeniging.

Suddenly our driver swerved into the driveway of a house and stopped in front of another van. He ordered us to stay in the car while he slipped into the house through a side door. We waited there for about an hour until a white man came out. Completely ignoring us, he went to stand at the gateway of the driveway, looking up and down the street.

After a while the driver darted out of the side door and stood a moment alongside the vans, looking towards the gate. I felt that he was waiting for a signal. We were all tensely silent. Suddenly he made for the van in front of us, and opened the door at the back. The two fellows in our van clambered out through the flowers and joined him.

Then they carried out carefully packed cartons, about six of them, from the other van into ours.

'Is that the hooch?' I asked my friend.

'Mmm,' he replied.

And I could hear the faint tinkle of clinking bottles. Inside our van they arranged the flowers carefully to hide away the cartons in case the door had to be opened. The two chaps at the back put newspapers over the cartons and sat on two of them.

Our driver looked towards the gate, then got into the van and backed slowly out. At the gate he dropped a key, and drove away.

'Surely that is not a bottle store, is it?' I asked.

The driver laughed a little. 'No,' he said, 'that was not a bottle store. That man was just a contact.'

'Ever been caught before?' I wanted to know.

He laughed again. 'No. Only once the Flying Squad took a look at our flowers. That's where doing it in daylight helps.'

They dropped us at the same corner of Diagonal and Sauer Streets.

My friend, who knew that I was doing a story for *Drum*, suddenly said: *'Ou Verwoerd notch skaars'*: (Verwoerd doesn't know a thing). These boys think of Dr Verwoerd as the government.

Oddly enough, most of the liquor that flows into the illicit trade does not come from Johannesburg City. It comes from suburban bottle stores. One shebeen queen travels as far as Kimberley, in the Cape, to get her liquor.

A usual technique is for the bottle store owner to

drive through a white suburb and note down all the vacant lots. Sometimes he collects addresses of dead people or people in gaol. By spreading it out he can enter into his books sales that do not seem too large, and still he can keep his shebeens fully supplied. Most bottle stores do not deal with individual shebeens. They supply dealers, who in turn supply shebeens.

Another source is the 'big time' operators who break into bottle stores, usually with inside help, generally a white man, who gives them the layout of the 'joint'.

Several bottle stores have been hit by the 'Hole-in-the-wall Gang'. Their method invariably has been that in order to make all the noise they please in breaking through a roof or wall without attracting unwelcome attention, someone has had to be silenced.

The wholesale merchant disposes of his liquor in one of two ways. He may either employ a runner who sells to the shebeen, or he may have his own shebeen where he sells the liquor.

Then there are small operators who employ white hoboes to procure the liquor for them. These democratic characters visit various bottle stores and make small purchases at each, and at the end of a day they are able to supply a runner with about six bottles of brandy. The police know about them, but there are so many of them going that it is difficult to keep track of all.

Last year about five illicit stills manufacturing brandy and beer were found on the Reef. Some of them were operated by Europeans, and some of them by Non-Europeans.

And last year, too, the cry had gone up: 'Let the Africans drink European Liquor!' On the whole, the police feel that their work would be considerably simplified if Africans were to be allowed light wines and beer. Many officials feel that crime would be reduced if Africans were allowed throughout the country to drink freely. The winegrowers are beginning to feel that the illicit trade in liquor cheats them of their fair share of the profits. And the Africans are increasingly showing their determination to get at European liquor.

The issue is no longer whether Africans in general should be allowed to drink. THEY DRINK IN ANY CASE. The issue is whether they may drink legally.

Prohibition has been proved impossible. There is too great a thirst for drink among the unentitled. And too great a thirst for money among the bottle store keepers. And prohibition is asking for too much from the police.

According to the 1954 Report of the Bureau of Census and Statistics, there were in general 1 542 415 prosecutions of which 1 373 589 ended in convictions. Of the 1 542 415 prosecutions, 950 415 were for liquor and habit-forming drugs; and of the 1 373 589 convictions, 886 601 were for liquor and habit-forming drugs.

This means that 62 per cent of the 1954 prosecutions were for liquor and habit-forming drugs, and 65 per cent of the convictions were for liquor and habit-forming drugs. It also means that 93 per cent of the liquor and drugs prosecutions ended in convictions.

In other words if the illicit liquor trade were to be stopped we could cut prosecutions and convictions very heavily. That could be cutting crime heavily!

The other day in a shebeen I was caught by members of the liquor squad with a nip of brandy. At the police station I was told I could pay an admission of guilt fine that was £5 for a bottle of brandy or part thereof. The police were very friendly. They told me that a man of my standing ought to apply for a liquor licence, and ought not to be found drinking in shebeens.

I paid £5 like thousands of other men of my standing caught in the same circumstances.

Poetry

O GHANA

Bright with the souls of our fathers,
Beneath whose shade we live and die,
Red for the blood of the heroes in the fight,
Green for the precious farms of our birthright,
And linked with these the shining golden band
That marks the richness of our Fatherland.
We'll live and die for Ghana.
Our land of hope for ages to come!
Shout it aloud, O Ghana,
And beat it out upon the drum!
Come from the pine-lined shore, from the broad
                                    northern plain,
From the farm and the forest, the mountain and mine,
Your children sing with ancient minstrel lore:
Freedom for ever for evermore!
This be our vow, O Ghana,
To live as one in unity,
And in your strength, O Ghana,
To build a new fraternity!
Africa waits in the night of the clouded years,

For the spreading light that now appears,
To give us all a place beneath the sun,
The destined ending of a task well done.

BALLAD TO THE COFFEE CART

A little tin shack on wheels,
Jars a Jo'burg pavement,
Like a busy ant the roadwife peels
Potatoes, stirs porridge, blind to enslavement.

It is the blackman's Coffee Cart,
Simpler, cheaper, more nourishing,
And, oddly, so near to the heart
Of this Metropolis' chestnut worker.

Coffee is the least of its wares;
Sour milk, Mahewu, dumpling and meat
Staples all — but I love most the democratic airs
Of the easy-smiling women who come to eat.

If only the guys with the burning meat,
And the slick restaurants where stomachs smart
Did not agitate against that dinner on the street,
You'd meet me during lunch at the Coffee Cart.

DEAR GOD

God, you gave me colour,
Rich, sun-drenched, chocolate,
And you gave me valour,

Enough for Love, for Hate.

But, God, Understanding
And Patience, and gazelle
Acceptance of Suffering . . .
You rather gave me Hell.

It's in affectionate
Names that I daily curse
The modes how You create:
Of Love, Hate, so perverse

That but for the untold
Wisdom which, only Thine,
Silences my revolt,
A spark from The Divine.

I'd be like Thee in wrath,
In Life's demolition
Or creation, and pronounce
Supreme imprecation . . . .

Dammit, God, I'm provoked
More than mortal or clod
Thy will at first evoked.
I'll thunder like you, God.

YOUR MAN'S BEEN CLAPPED . . .

Your man's been clapped in jail,
    but you're a nice-time kid,
Your man's been clapped in jail, but
    you're a nice-time kid,

Your man's been clapped in jail, but
   you're a nice-time kid,
You can make with your love-life what
   you will.

Y-YES, DARLING

'You're the green pastures and the
   blooming flora of the Earth . . . . '

'Y-Yes, darling.'
'You're the bird-like creature that
   floats in the heavens and fills the
   air with song . . . . '

'Y-Y-Yes, love.'
'You're the blue sky, so pure, so
   serene . . . . '
'And, love, you are —'
'You are Sputnik streaking into the
   empyrean, into Space . . .

'Oh, my darling!'
' . . . shooting into space beyond your
   promises.'

I COULDN'T . . . .

I couldn't take a piece of candy from
   a kid . . .
I couldn't hurt a fly, nor even a flea . . .

I couldn't steal a man, not even from
   my worst girl-foe . . .

I couldn't gold-dig a decent man —
   but, heavens, they're so willing!

PART TWO

Personalities

THE LIFE AND LOVE OF
DOLLY RATHEBE

Dolly and Her Men

'The first and most exciting man in my life, dear
Can, was my father. I can't imagine any man having
greater influence on me. I simply worshipped him
but, like all other things one considers sacred, he
didn't last long. After his death men didn't seem
the same to me; they seemed to have lost that manly
tang, that rough, tough, solid masculinity that makes
men so adorable. Nowadays men have become catty,
peevish, gossipy and mean; women have taken to
wearing slacks.' So says 28-year-old Dolly Rathebe,
just about Africa's most famous and exciting woman
torch singer. And yet she is not Dolly Rathebe at all.
She was born Josephine Malatsi. That's her real name.

When Dolly was still at school she had a friend
whose name was Dolly Rathebe. Our Dolly loved her
so much that she just took over her name and called
herself Dolly Rathebe. And that is how the world
came to know her. This Dolly Rathebe — the real one
— is none other than Eileen Dolly Rathebe, the
daughter of Mr J R Rathebe. She later went to Fort

Hare, where she gained the BSc degree. She is now
married to medical student Edward Makhene who is
studying at the University of the Witwatersrand. The
film-star Dolly Rathebe just took over her friend's
name for the fun of it. But back of it all was the
uncertainty Dolly felt about conditions at home.
Things were beginning to bust up.

And at school Dolly was a tomboy. (She was
fond of boys!) She looked at life from the male
point of view and seemed to have a quarrel with her
Maker for creating her female. At one time the
reverend father at St Cyprian's, Sophiatown, where
Dolly schooled, wanted someone to go up the tower
and release the hammer of the bell that had got
caught. Without hesitation Dolly clambered up the
tower and loosened the hammer. The boys still talk
of the 'worm's-eye view' they got on that occasion.

But she was smart. Always trim and neatly dressed,
she looked as if she came from a very good and
decent home. Suddenly, however, her parents died
within a short time of each other, and Dolly had to
face a hard, cruel world alone. She discovered that
she had a fairly good voice, mellow and husky, and
she toyed with the idea of showbusiness. First she
started with that old theatre of African jazz, the
street. At that time Sophiatown was different from
what it is now. It looked more or less like a country
dorp. People were still planting peach and apricot
trees in their backyards. In fact, one of Dolly's great
pastimes was to pinch peaches from the backyards of
other people. And when she and her young friends
had made a good haul they would go to Macauvlei —
a waste dump just outside Sophiatown, near Waterval
— make a feast of it, and start jitterbugging. Jitterbug
held the place then that is held by jive now. They

would hop around and kick their legs out to the
rhythm of some catchy tune. It is about this time
that Dolly discovered that she had a way of stitching
a tune to the rhythm of their dancing. Of course,
nobody at that time thought that Dolly had the voice
to coo the blues through the hearts of a thousand
stage-goers. To her friends she was just a boyish little
kid who talked gruffly and sang just as gruffly the
hits that went by.

But all agree that she was a naughty child, 'very,
very impossible,' as one of her teachers describes her.
She was fond of pulling chairs from under other
children, putting nails or drawing pins on their sitting
places, attaching 'Kick Me' notices to their behinds,
getting a great thrill from watching their pained
reactions. Still, at this time she did not consider boys
as lovers. She thought of them and treated them as
pals. Oddly enough, she rather liked them. She liked
their rough-riding, rollicking sense of fun. She
gambolled with them, pushed them around, got
pushed around, played the African version of hide-and-
seek called *Blikmampatile* with them.

Somehow in this wild young life she met Jeff. He
was the direct opposite of Dolly. Quiet, dignified,
halting of speech, shy, studious, well-behaved. But
they fell in love. That was Dolly's earliest crush. She
loved him with a wild, reckless abandon. 'Jeff had
something, Can. He represented everything that in my
secret moments I dreamed, hoped, yearned to become.
I should have known that I wasn't made like that. For
me life has always been too raw, too rough, too full
of fun and trigger-quick happiness. And I have little
time for the gushing, sentimental spurts in human
affairs. I have learned early enough to be tough and
grabbing about the things I want from life. But Jeff . . .

Jeff . . . dearest Jeff . . . .'

Unfortunately Jeff was just a flitting lightning
flash. Sophiatown has never been a comfortable home
for sweet easy love affairs. The strong men had to
notice Dolly some time or other. One day Hasie,
tough, hard-hitting filibuster, met Dolly as she was
going home from school, and he took a fancy to her.
In the great old Sophiatown tradition he hit her into
loving him. 'You're hurting me,' she moaned. 'Ah, if
you want me to love you, just say the word, and it's
all right, but don't hit me so hard.' And so they were
in love.

For a time it was thrilling to be a strong-man's
moll. The other girls envied her, the other men laid
off, and she could go to shows and movies when she
liked, unmolested, and without being interfered with.
But too soon it began to pall. Dolly discovered that
many people whom she would have liked to accept
her began to look askance at her. It wasn't quite the
thing to be known as a gangster's girl. Moreover,
Hasie was beginning to become jealously possessive.
She couldn't even talk to other men, and Dolly, who
loved life and the dynamics of vital men, started to
feel stifled. But it wasn't easy to break away from a
strong man, least of all a touchy guy like Hasie.

It had to take death — swift, brutal, bloody death —
to end the unhappy love affair. Like all strong men.
Hasie had made many enemies. One afternoon he
went with a handful of friends to Alexandra on a
nice-time spree. They had more than a couple of
drinks and Hasie started throwing his weight around.
That gave his enemies just the break they wanted.
They staged a quarrel and a fight broke out. Hasie
got stabbed and died before he could get back home.
That released Dolly from her affair with him.

There were, however, many other young lovelorn lads who were gasping for Dolly in secret anguish. But they didn't quite have the guts to go up to her and declare their hearts. Ellison Mhlongo, lately a respectable teacher in the now dead St. Peter's Secondary School, Rosettenville, in Johannesburg, once lamented to me: 'The trouble with Dolly Rathebe at this prank-playing stage of her life was that she was an incurable hoaxer. Those of us who loved her in secret wouldn't dare make advances to her for fear of becoming the laughing-stock of the whole school for a week or two. So we sat back and just mournfully watched her gallivanting through the day. But in a certain sense we were proud of her too. We admired the restless, reckless energy of that little dynamo of mischief; we loved to see her among us boys, climbing into trees, clambering over fences, leaping and laughing for the sheer joy of it, and then suddenly breaking into a breezy tune and dance. For her pure joyfulness we often forgave her all the pranks she ever played on us. That's the Dolly I knew.'

She started performing in school troupes, but the sedate, well-organised music of school choirs did not quite go with her. She wanted the pounding rhythm that interpreted township life so well. Already at fifteen/sixteen she felt the throb of location life's many-splendoured thrill, and she sought a medium through which she might get the sizzle out of her. The choral music of school life with its neatly arranged formations and its gym-dressed dreariness was hopelessly inadequate for her. It didn't seem to get to the pulsating heart of things. It had nothing to say about the swift knife, the heady hangovers, the bitter, swearing quarrels, the reckless laughter, the stolen kisses, and wet, messy sex.

And then suddenly the unpredictable Dolly turned goo-goo good. She was an ardent girl guide and entered into all the activities of the Girl Guide movement. She loved going on parade, going camping, or just going about the streets of Sophiatown in her smart, always neat, Girl Guide uniform. Then she also went in for Sunday school teaching believe you me. For a spell she was a Bible-reading blues mama. But she took her Bible-reading seriously. And the little kids just loved her. She used to teach them simple hymns, and she managed to put into the hymns tingling little rhythm effects. Later, she was to thrill mourners at the wakes of dead friends with her singing. The 'wake' in Sophiatown is a social institution that breaks down all the annoying little class barriers and acts of snobbery. Everybody goes to the wake, and it doesn't matter so awfully much if you don't know the dear departed. You go to a wake to enjoy the evening, just as you often speak of 'a very nice funeral'.

Then you sing hymns throughout the night in the company of murderers and thieves singing lustily, in the midst of shebeen queens and prostitutes wailing feelingly. And now and then some devout old man would say a prayer as if his audience were regular churchgoers. Well, Dolly loved going to wakes and funerals, and she added her sob and her song to the services. In a sense, to her, they were sort of night-spots. It was at one of these wakes that she met Georgie. This was in the winter of 1945. It was a cold wet night, but inside the house in Bertha Street, Sophiatown, it was stuffy and she would go out now and then for a little air. During one of these excursions she saw Georgie outside and they fell into a conversation. She thought he was a nice guy and he saw in her a sweet girl. Early in the morning he walked her home over into Western Township. After that occasion they met several times. It was a quiet cinema-going, hand-clasping love affair. Dolly liked Georgie a lot, but somehow he lacked the fire and the zest she had begun to crave for in her lovers. Nothing was deeply wrong with Georgie, only he didn't fling her into spasms and thrilling sensations. Hardly three months were out before she felt that they were drifting apart. The stage was claiming more and more of her time, and after she had gone on another of her Bloemfontein trips she stopped seeing him. He made a few lame attempts to patch up their love affair, but he ultimately realised that you can't harness a race-horse with a mule!

So in 1943, with Standard Five uncompleted, Dolly left school to try her chances in the rough and tumble of township life. But from the beginning she was different from the domestic-servant, factory-working type of girl. She saw herself as an artist and she just wouldn't go to work. Not for a white man, that is. She went to live with an aunt in Western Township and for a time she was reasonably happy. Men did not trouble her much at this stage and now and then she managed to get a job or go on tour. She was very fond of Bloemfontein and used to go out there pretty often.

She wanted men at her feet, gazing up at her in awed admiration. She wanted the limelight, the spot-light, the searchlight even, so long as she could stand there alone selling her wares in tuneful magic. She knew she had a husky, furry voice that kindled in men's hearts strange desires and flashed before their tired, after-work imaginations dreams of torrid love and wanton abandon. And she knew more. She knew that a wiggle of her hips inbued a suggestive phrase of song with infinite seductiveness. Dolly was to be the girl who would bring a new force to the African stage. Rhythm and melody it already had. But the performers stood there in dull potato rows and sang dull soprano or dead alto or dinning tenor or drowning bass. But not Dolly. She went before her audience and treated them to live, wriggling flesh and she purred to them in a shaggy, hairy, deep, sultry mezzo. And she sang to them of the unachieved, half-realised longings of their own lives.

There is an old saying in showbusiness: 'Any stage artist who can hit it off with the Sophiatown audience has made the grade, but definitely.' The Sophiatown audience is just about the hardest-hearted, the cruel-lest, the most prejudiced, the most hostile audience God has created to plague the lives of musicians. Many great performers have cracked before that audience. They don't like the 'Chiramborara' of the Manhattan Brothers. They don't like the molly-coddling sentimentalism of 'Sout' of the bawdah.' They don't like the clatter of tap-dancing. They don't like nothing and they don't like no one. But they turn up to your shows and get there just to boo. Well, Dolly started there determined to break the iron in the heart of Sophiatown. She is the great stage personality that she is today just because she fought the hardest school of showbusiness. And she won. Of course, Sophiatown now gives Dolly grudging acclaim. They recognise that she has got in where angels fear to tread.

After her first fiery debut in Sophiatown she went in for night-clubs. In white Johannesburg Dolly became the entertainment darling. Nightly she performed

for the bleary-eyed patrons of those night-clubs. One
night she was returning from a show by car together
with the Manhattan Brothers. Suddenly zoomed along
the Flying Squad and stopped them. The police
searched their car but found no dangerous weapons,
no illicit liquor. They demanded their night passes.
Dolly and her friends had none, and they were locked
up for the night. Looking back at the incident, Dolly
is quite philosophical about it. 'What can I care
about things like that. You know, the Flying Squad
virtually lives with us, and nowadays you're not a full-
grown man if you haven't been arrested at least once.
Anyhow, what have I to grumble about when even
chiefs are being arrested for passes these days!'

Dolly in Films

You must know one thing. When a girl hits the top
with the general public, to certain brands of Africans
she becomes the 'fair prize' for the man who can
throw the muscle — or swing the knife, or squeeze the
trigger. To Dolly Rathebe this kind of thing came
earlier than to most girls, maybe because she was one
of the first to hit the public silly. She had become the
crazy stage girl who now and then delighted concert
audiences with her lively style and stagecraft. Hitherto, 'concerts' meant affairs in which very proper
four-voice groups would behave their music from the
stage and take very proper bows to mark their exits.
Not so Dolly Rathebe. She used the stage as if every
square inch belonged to her; as if she were a boxer
in a ring and her art depended on her ability to prove
that she had a life lease on it.

So here came a new factor to the African stage.

New? Well, people who performed sketches and ragtimes had long before her used movement on the stage. But that was a set, thought-out-before movement which had to be repeated in exact detail at every performance. Dolly's movements were directed by mood and feeling and climate, and you never knew what that dame would do next but you knew it would be right. Why, Dolly had become an actress! This was not the self-conscious, stage-directed kind of acting. It was an unconscious desire to interpret the crawling fullness and ever-changing variety of township life. And because she enacted her songs, rather than just recited them, Dolly rode the merry-go-round with her audiences.

She was so alive and reflexive to every tang in township life that her growing fans thought of her as *rats* (quick on the up-take), and for short they called her Katz. So everywhere the word went round that the new stage-cry was Dolly Katz Rathebe. Of course at that time showbusiness was not nearly the big-time industry it is now fast becoming. There was therefore not the refreshing encouragement that comes from high-powered competition and big business. Most of those people who continued in showbusiness did it for the love of the thing. But Dolly Rathebe sensed even in the Forties that she was on to a great outlet.

'I tell you, Can, in those jitterbug days I saw a future for Black entertainment. Not so much in the singing and performing of the artists, but in the gusto with which the public flung itself into the wild hop and shuffle of the dance,' Dolly told me cheerfully. But she knew that she was still small-time. She knew that the big breaks had not yet come. But she also knew that she had something new, something many

of the other performers of her day had not caught on
to yet. She could make every song of hers a story. A
story full of the magic of the life that she knew.

Meanwhile, she hobnobbed with various small
troupes. First she was having her fun. She was in
showbusiness, what could matter more? But soon, all
too soon, she realised that those troupes were
cramping her original style, that desire of not merely
howling a song, but acting it, re-enacting in it the
social riddles that had been so much of her life.

And she was frustrated. So in her private life she
went on the rocks. Men were crowding her left and
right. Some were interested in her romantically, but
others wanted to rough her up. Sophiatown, Western
Township, Newclare — Johannesburg as a whole
became too hot for Dolly, unless she met toughness
with toughness. And that is just what she decided to
do. The general impression of Dolly Rathebe as a
Jo'burg rough-house mama is grossly unfair. When she
fought anybody, it was just for the right to exist.
If she got to a concert in town or in the locations, it
was a hit-and-run matter whether she would get home
in one piece. But if you belong to 'Softown' —
nothing soft about it — you can always get by. One
evening Dolly was scheduled to sing at the BMSC.
The show itself was just ordinary, nothing special to
highlight it, and there was no such legend as 'the
great Dolly', nobody thought in those terms as yet.
But when she came out, after the show, there was a
black car waiting . . . . Now, transportation is the
great bugbear of show business, especially when the
show is held in town. So when there magically
appears a car to transport you home, you don't
hesitate.

So Dolly rushed for the offer of a lift home.

Though the driver had his own girl with him in the
car, he lost his head over the fact that Dolly Rathebe
was in the car. But the plot had not been his really.
The fellows who had hired the car had made the
original design to 'take Dolly for a ride'. Suddenly
suspicious, Dolly enquired who exactly had offered
her the lift home. Some grunt from the back admitted
that he had been responsible. 'I have known you from
schooldays,' he grunted further. But Dolly instantly
felt sure that she had not known the guy from the
first coming of Christ.

Without arguing with them, without asking further
questions, she yanked the door of the car open, and
made a dash for it. She didn't have to walk all the
way to the Western Areas. At the taxi rank in town
she found a taxi that was taking people to some
northern European suburbs before he could offer to
take her home. But she got home all right that night.

Her love affairs of this period were like wisps of
smoke. One moment thick and meaningful, the next
moment gone and forgotten. Still, there was the rest
of life to be fought.

Rightly or wrongly, Dolly came to feel that all the
antagonism against her was the result of jealousy,
private jealousy of petty people who wondered why
they could not take the place she held under the
spotlight. And she fought back fiercely. Most of the
other girls thought that Dolly was really out to
swallow their boyfriends or that she was becoming
too popular in the atmosphere of their boyfriends —
with evil designs, they suggested. But these were the
kind of quarrels that are not usually carefully argued
out. Before anybody gets the chance to put the case,
nails fly cuttingly, and knives are drawn.

Edie clashed with Dolly at a party. Edie thought

that Dolly was forward with the men at a certain Sophiatown party, and did not like it. Dolly thought Edie was one of those women who hated her just because she was a star. No one really knows what set the explosion off. They had a violent fight that tumbled the tables and scattered the partygoers. For the first time something of Dolly's ungovernable temper, always lying still beneath her child-like naiveté, burst out. She fought like a bereaved tigress until people of courage managed to break it up.

But all Dolly has to say about that fight today is that Edie was full of 'nonsense' and in any case she herself was still mad in those days.

She went on, though, trying to perfect that gimmick of hers of injecting a bit of acting into her singing. One day a film producing company decided for the first time to make a film with an all-African cast, and an all-African theme. They produced the story of a country lad coming to Johannesburg for the first time and going through all the hazards of Johannesburg life. Finally, he lands in the Ngoma Club and, having a good voice, he gets a part to sing there. He meets a fabulous nightclub singer swathed in snake-like, seductive rolls of glittering dress. And she sings a song that has a special tug at his heart for it says the things his heart would have liked to say:

> Jo'burg City, the Golden City,
> What did I come here for?
> Oh, Jo'burg City, the Golden City,
> I'm far away from my home.'

But the makers of the film wanted an African woman who could play the lead part. A talent scout, Sam Alcock, brought them Dolly Rathebe. She was auditioned, tested, adjudged, rolled over and out, and

she made the grade. Maybe she's all that we've got in
Africa, but she was all Africa. That, in the end, and
her wonderful, furry voice, and her serpentine figure
got her the part.

The film was *Jim Comes To Jo'burg,* the first
all-African film ever to be made in South Africa.
And it was a terrific hit. White South Africa gasped to
see, in 1949, that the sheer event was dreamworthy.
Black South Africa thrilled at the idea that black
faces, black life, black background, could appear on
the screen. Overnight the name of Dolly Rathebe
was flashed acrosss the countryside. Imagine it! A
black girl of Johannesburg appeared on the big
posters, hoardings, and placards of blinking cinema
fronts. And in the film, they said, when she sang, she
sang like the low humming of a slow-moving river.
'We must go to see *Jim Comes To Jo'burg!'* Even
people who normally thought that the bioscope was
not quite the place where decent people went for
their entertainment, they went in their thousands to
see Dolly Rathebe in *Jim Comes To Jo'burg.*

So-and-so in Such-and-such! It just sounded like
the real films. It sounded as if Africa was being
transported into the fascinating world of Hollywood.
And to us Hollywood did not mean divorces and a
wild life. It meant glamour and wealth and idolatry.
A few of us in the know about this film business
were asking, How many thousands of pounds does
Dolly earn now? How many gowns and palaces does
she own? How many fan letters does she get? But for
the rest of us she was a spangled, glitter-spattered
star, up above the heavens so high.

What did this sudden upthrust into glory do to
Dolly? Did it fill her head with boiled water, and
make her strut like a peacock? Nix! Dolly came right

back to us and remained the impetuous Sophiatown kid she'd always been. But there was a new poise and grace about her.

She came back to showbusiness and its lesser world from the heights of stardom. But she came back a star. That made a difference. Her stage appearances were henceforth heralded events. They drew the glamour-stunned as well as the merely curious.

But the success of *Jim Comes To Jo'burg* encouraged film-makers to chance another picture soon. This was a light comedy, again in the setting of township life, and it was called *The Magic Garden*. It reflected the quaint, little superstitions of African life, the spontaneous humour — humour no more, because such an inseparable part of African life. The story is that of a thief who buries money in somebody's garden, and the poor family on the brink of starvation, digging in their garden, find the money. The money is the thread throughout the story. It gets into various hands, but ultimately enables the hero, Victor Qwayi, to pay the bride-price for his beloved Dolly Rathebe. The marriage that follows is a typical rollicking township affair of singing and dancing, and Dolly Rathebe is the soul of it all. Tommy Ramokgopa, is the comic thief, and to see him is to burst into uncontrollable fits of laughter and to recognise the irrepressible location street urchin.

The Magic Garden was directed by Donald Swanson and became a famed film throughout the world. Perhaps, as much as anything else, it is the one medium that has presented urban Africa to the world, and for once the world did not have to shake or hang its head about Africa. It joined in the side-bursting laughter.

By this time Dolly Rathebe was accepted as
a great artist. She was no more just a fluke, an
accident that occurred in South Africa. So she got
attached to big-time bands like the Harlem Swing-
sters and went touring the country. This was good
for Dolly and this was good for the country. Dolly
needed the publicity of appearing in the flesh before
her thousands of admirers to prove that she was not
just a dolled up puppet; the country was thirsting
to meet its great heroine.

In the beginning of 1952 a new magazine for Non-
European people discovered Dolly and her charms as
a pin-up girl. This magazine noticed that Dolly
Rathebe had just the contours and curves to gloss
and gush from a magazine.

They sent out their photographer to track her
down and take some bathing costume pictures of her.
He drove her out on to the mine dumps armed with
a load of costumes and clothes. Meanwhile a police
van had been following them all the time. Just when
the photographer had completed taking his pictures
and Dolly was dressing back to normal, the police
appeared and questioned them as to what they were
up to. The photographer was taken to the police
station and questioned, but it could not be proved
that anything more than the camera's eye had peeked
at Dolly's luscious figure.

That new magazine was *Drum*.

Dolly in Jo'burg's White Night-clubs

When Dolly Rathebe first became a magazine model,
her bikini pictures were so hot that they formed the
subject of heated controversy for long, talkative

months. Better still, at that time there were completely unfounded rumours that Dolly had married. So
many people were splitting their collars over 'this
young mother who is such an awful example to
teenage girls.' But Dolly went her showbiz way
merrily.

She was learning something new in the Non-
European entertainment world: that there was no
such thing as bad publicity. An entertainer just must
keep in the public eye or bust. It does not matter
whether he gets slated for some indiscreet act, or
some thoughtless scrape — so long as he gives the
public food for garrulous gossip, they will always die
to go and see the fabulous character who was involved
in such-and-such a scandal.

And Dolly had the personality and the character to
be thoroughly talked about. This bounced upon the
newspaper world, for now everything Dolly did or
said became 'hot news'. and so she got more and
more publicity. These, then, are the things that
zinged Dolly into the skies: she had made two
successful movie films, and she had become the
publicity star number one. In one of her films, *Jim
Comes to Jo'burg*, she appears as a night-club torch
singer, where she wilted her audience with a sultry
number called 'Jo'burg City, the Golden City.' Her
performance at the Ngoma Club must have caught
the eyes of some of Johannesburg's most enterprising
night-club owners.

For in a short while she became one of the most
sought-after singers in the city's white night-clubs.
Then she fell into the hands of that old entertainment
trouper, Alfred Herbert. He groomed her and many
other Non-European performers for the peculiarly
delicate work of night-club entertainment. Long

before people dreamed of the romping rhythms of township jazz Herbert had them cooing and crooning and capering before white night-lifers.

In 1954, Alfred Herbert threw his Windmill Theatre shows in Johannesburg. In themselves they were not terribly successful, but they are now of tremendous importance because they gave birth to African Jazz, the real precursor to Township Jazz. Here then Dolly was trained in the poise and grace that the highly personalised, the close-up atmosphere of night-club work, exacted. It gave her finish and polish, but it did not rub out the vital effervescence of her jazziness. Alf Herbert is shrewd. He knew many of his patrons in the night-clubs were young Jewish men and women. So he got Dolly to sing a couple of Yiddish songs. Sing to a man in the language of his own soul, searchingly stirring the deep-down yearnings, and you sing the blues. But sing to a man in the language of his own race, even though haltingly, and you make that man the slave of your art. In a short while Dolly Rathebe was on the lips of every white sophisticate in Johannesburg. Those people who had no idea of the untapped wealth in the townships were humming Dolly's songs, were thinking of this black marvel of a girl who thrilled them each night and soothed their cares away. And, brother, that meant connections. It meant, for one thing, that every time night-club owners wanted a hot torch singer that was also a kind of an oddity, a new thrill, they found they knew only Dolly Rathebe. And so she got jobs in night-club after night-club, and the goose was laying the golden eggs by mass production.

At last the profession of the stage was beginning to pay in a real comfy way. A subtle transformation was coming over Dolly Rathebe, the human being, too.

She was dressing more elegantly, she deported herself with more dignity, and she had learned the culture of that shadow-world of night-clubs and night-cats to the syllable. In her rolling mezzo, she talked of the denizens of that world. 'Say, bub, I mean I had the cats rocked the other night and they kept screaming for more. *Eintlik*, man bub, when I'm Jewish and mesten, and I croon at the cats, I go in for the kill.' When Dolly Rathebe is dressed to death, and she sings her blues wooingly, she does kill her audience.

Still, privately, all was not completely dovetailed in her life. She still didn't have a real home. She still flitted from township room to township room. She still couldn't find the man who'd be all her own. And she found that the only kick out of life she could get among the only friends she could make, came from the fire-water that they sell in Johannesburg's shebeens. All very well to perform for tuxedoed whites in posh night-clubs. There are no real night-clubs for blacks in this man's town.

True, there's the Bantu Men's Social Centre. But that is a man's world, and to Dolly that is a place for work, a place where she sang to her black brothers. There's no place where a hard-singing girl might find relaxation. No place except the shebeen.

So Dolly, like so many of us, took to drinking. Hard, heavy drinking, with a brutal vengeance against the life that crowded her among the ruffians, amid the ragamuffins. She went in for gin. And she baptised it Three-times-a-day. The name came from the doctor's prescription that you've got to take three times a day, but Dolly never bothered to shake the bottle. It was a grim commentary on the number of times per day that she needed to be pepped up.

It was on many a late night that Dolly was seen

going home reeling. She got into scraps and fights.
She clashed with other girls and about other girls'
boyfriends. She went in for rowdyism as if she was
paid for it. But she soon learned to take her liquor
and hold it down. Now that she has outgrown reckless
drinking and reckless living, Dolly has given many
young, up-and-coming girls good advice on 'knowing
your limits'.

Dolly also went in for record-making. She made a
record called *Into yam* which went to the heads of
all township urchins. And that's the way to make and
sell a record. Get the wild waifs of the township crazy
over it. The lyrics told the story of a girl who loves
her man even though he is a drunk because at least
he works for her. But the music wasn't thick and
blue. It rippled joyfully and forced your feet to
twinkle into a wheel-spoke dance.

And if you don't dance, the background chorus
that goes on naggingly, 'Iyo! Iyo! Iyo! Iyo!' has got
to get you. Dolly took this song of her record on to
the stage and showed the world how to dance. She
went onto the stages of the BMSC and the Odin
Cinema with loons like Nice Molantoa, Jarvis Disemelo,
and the rest of the rough and tumble, and she would
do her stuff. She had a trick of turning her rearguard
to the audience and flicking her most pronounced
protruberance in a naughty provocative way, and she
called it, 'Do with the buttocks.' That brought the
house out of their seats.

Then she met Mboy. He belonged to one of the
slickest, best-dressed groups of young men in Sophiatown. He was young and handsome and smart — but
most important of all — hopelessly in love with
Dolly. So in love, in fact, that he coined a new
expression in the lingo of the townships. At that time

whenever anybody greeted you, he said: *'Is hoe daar?'* (How's it there?) and you replied: *'Is dolly'* which meant 'It's swell'. Mboy extended the expression: *'Is hoe daar?'* you would say, and back he'd come with *'Is Dolly Rathebe.'* It caught on, and had its ephemeral days in fashion as tsotsi lingo.

Soon there were wild-fire rumours that Dolly and Mboy were married. After all, they were living together, so people jumped to the one illogical conclusion. But these rumours were hopelessly unfounded. They were just two love-birds for whom marriage was utterly unnecessary. Not long after, the stork called and they had a baby girl and they called the little darling Zola. Dolly is just crazy about Zola and dreams the most fantastic things for her. In fact she was thrilled to the marrow when she heard the other day that Zola had been performing on stage at a school concert. Clear case of history repeating itself!

But Dolly's work took her away a great deal, and by little creeping inches she was drifting away from Mboy. In the meanwhile Zola was staying with her paternal grandmother, and daddy was no more staying at home in Sophiatown. Dolly left her room in Meyer Street, went to stay with an aunt in Orlando. But the call of the stage was strong, and Alfred Herbert was toying with a dashingly new idea. No less than a Jazz Train to Durban. Wow, what an idea. All the cast of African Jazz Parade were preparing for this mammoth trip, and do you think Dolly Rathebe thought of being left behind?

Dolly from Place to Place with African Jazz

Yes, the fertile mind of the entertainment world,

Alfred Herbert, was sending the whole African Jazz troupe to Durban to give that city a shot in the arm. They were going by train from Johannesburg and that gave the trip a new gloss of glamour. Not only were the boys and girls going to jazz up Durban, they were also going to chirp all along their way there. It was quite an affair, a cross between a jazz tour and a splashing holiday.

I went to the Johannesburg station to see them off. They were like a fun-mad group of picknickers. There was 'King Jeff' Jarvis Disemelo playing the fool with everybody; Tandi Mpambani so demure with her faraway look in the eyes; Skip Phahlane intoning his mock-Xhosa; Mavis Roach breathing her rock-bottom blues; her guitar-twanging husband, Billy, then genial-faced Gene Williams, now languishing or lashing out in Britain, and the Midnight Kids, and the Cuban Brothers.

But Dolly Rathebe was the Aladdin Lamp of the lot. She radiated a glow of happiness that I had not seen in her for months, and every now and then she sparked off bursts of carefree laughter. I knew then a crisis in her life had passed and her spirit was convalescing beautifully.

The train trip was a songful surfeit of off-stage abandon. Saxophones were moaning, trumpets were blaring, basses were groaning, and strident female voices were shrieking. Of course, Dolly's voice isn't exactly female.

But all this was preparatory to the big shows in Durban. They did Durban thoroughly, and the rave notices were full of praise. Dolly emerged as the great star of the shows from the point of view of the press.

Of course, for some reason or other, Alfred Herbert's shows always got the press screaming with delight, but there's no denying it, in African Jazz Parade he had something that got under the skin of audiences, especially white audiences.

But then they had fun in between shows, mostly on the beach. There were those boys and girls, who ever so seldom see the beach and the sea, gambolling on the sand and splashing in the water. Perhaps it was this taste of the coast that finally won Dolly's love for the sea. On previous occasions there were always stinging thoughts of things not going so well at home or in her life that spoiled life for her. From now on she was going to enjoy coastal towns.

But back in Johannesburg one of the flashiest gangs, the Americans, were breaking up with internal fights. Dolly had been closely associated as a friend with this group of highly wardrobed young men. With the break-up came pitched battles, and one by one the police were picking them up and sending them to the Fort to go and cool off.

Everything turned nerve-rackingly uneasy for Dolly again, and Sophiatown was becoming too sticky for her. She tried to live in Orlando for some time, but this space-speed girl found life there too tardy, too suburban.

So she tried Alexandra.

It was there that she met Arthur Magerman. Well-built, excruciatingly handsome with a beard that ran into side whiskers, light as a peach. Arthur was one of the first railway clerks who joined the Government's scheme of using Non-Europeans as ticket clerks and barrier attendants. And he was not too shy to go making whoopee with Dolly. It was no rare sight to see them whizzing past at night from a show going to look for a nice-time party and in a car that flew like a dirt-track demon.

I do not think Dolly was genuinely — and so help
me God — in love with Arthur. He was just a handsome Apollo who stormed the citadel of her reserve.
If he got a thrill from being seen around with the
fabulous Dolly Rathebe, she herself liked the company
of so beautiful a man. But at least it had the outward
trappings of a gay romance.

Still, not only Sophiatown but, it appears, the
whole of Johannesburg was becoming too hot for
Dolly. There was a story during the jazz train days
that the Spoilers — the gang that took over Jo'burg's
underworld when all the other gangs had folded up —
were gunning for Dolly Rathebe.

The story even went so far as to suggest the Spoilers
intended to kidnap Dolly and she needed police
protection. Of course, the word 'kidnap' has a subtly
different meaning in township lingo. It does not mean
carrying off somebody for ransom. It merely means
to abduct. 'I want to kidnap that baby,' means I want
to duck away with her for a night or a couple of days,
most likely with her willing co-operation.

But Dolly denies vehemently that she had ever
been threatened with kidnapping. She did, however,
run out of Johannesburg, she did go to live in Port
Elizabeth where she met Welcome Duru, dapper,
slender singer with the Basin Blues Combo. And again
she fell in love. Dolly tells me that Welcome is the
end of the line. Not wishing to sound sarcastic, I
make no comment.

Life in Port Elizabeth was quiet for Dolly. She was
the queen all right. And somehow in all these out-
lying places Dolly was always lionised. Jo'burgers
tend to sneer at this celebrity business, but in places
like Port Elizabeth, East London, Cape Town, Dolly
Rathebe is Africa's star. Welcome Duru was a young

man, 19 years old. He had made a couple of records, and he was the leader of the Basin Blues Combo in Port Elizabeth. They were not by a long stretch the ace musicians of Port Elizabeth, and it's a wonder that Dolly who had been the throb and thrill of large halls and gaping crowds could be content with small time stuff in a hick town.

It is all the more wonder when one remembers that this is the period 1955 to 1956, the period in which the musical world in Johannesburg was trying new things. First there was talk of bringing out the magic of the jazz in the townships and presenting it elegantly before the rest of Johannesburg. An organisation which called itself the Union of South African Artists was set up. One of its main aims was to bring to light the cream of non-European talent and to make sure that these artists got a square deal. Every crooner and mooner, every tooter and twanger in the musical world was getting excited over this new trend. But Dolly was still in Port Elizabeth twiddling her thumbs. Out of nowhere, it seemed, came new thrushes to woo the vacant palace of music that our Doll seemed to have deserted.

And the first wave of Township Jazz overwhelmed Johannesburg. The rave reviews were ecstatic, and some of them must have reached the Sleeping Doll in Port Elizabeth for at last she stirred. She still didn't like Johannesburg, but Johannesburg doesn't ask to be liked, it seeks to be served. 'Welcome,' she said one day, 'the boys in Jozi are having a big time and they invite me to join the band. I guess a gal's gotta go.'

'Sure,' replied Welcome, 'and know what sweets? I'm coming along.' Just like that. But the public was yearning to know how the great Dolly would stand up against the new dazzling names.

This was Township Jazz II. When Dolly took the stage of the Selborne Hall, Johannesburg, in a hugging evening gown, she was cool, she trod with the feline grace of a panther, and she cooed with the warmth and sincerity of an accomplished artist. The years, far from staling her, had given her a soft dignity that awed you into idolatry. The past piquancy, the vitality, the reckless, rushing torrents of her darting eruptions were controlled and disciplined into an appeal that had to be heeded. Yes, Dolly Rathebe still had it. But she had grown up. She said to me just about this time: 'Even the wild life I led has gone out of me. It seems all so pointless. So juvenile. I'm surprised that many of my old friends are still running riot. It's all right for the youngsters who have just stepped on the stage. I suppose they must get the poison out of their systems first. But I'm tired. I want the deeper things in life.'

'And what kind of life would give you the deeper things, Dolly?' I asked curiously.

She looked at me, through me, far far away, maybe to Port Elizabeth. Then she said softly, 'A man who wants and offers security. Some guy who wants Zola, my daughter. A home where I can lay my weary head after the strains of night life. I can't find all the words for it, Can. But it's a kind of peace.'

In Johannesburg they lived in the posh Merabe Hotel, owned by businessman Mofokeng.

During her time with Township Jazz she managed to go to Durban again. Whilst the others went by train, Dolly flew. They were quite a success with Durban, but don't seem to have been as great a hit with the Durban public as African Jazz.

One thing I'm sure of though, is that the kind of peace Dolly wants is not the peace of death. There is

too much township in her, too much stage. When
Alfred Herbert returned from a successful tour of the
Cape and Natal, he found Township Jazz and Dolly in
it making whoopee. He listened to it for a while. It was
not quite his cup of tea, but he recognised that they
had something. Herbert's kind of African jazz, his
version of the business, was to put on the stage all
you got, all your rhythm. Maybe a girl or two or a
crooner to give with the harmony. But it's the great,
rippling ocean of rhythm behind that should pound
the temples of his audience. He had it, but he felt he
didn't quite have it co-ordinated. He didn't quite have
a Dolly. And after all, he reasoned, Dolly had been of
his own making.

Queen of Song!

When Alf Herbert came back to Johannesburg after a
breezy coastal tour with his African Jazz, he found
the city still throbbing with after-tremors of Township
Jazz. And he found Dolly at the centre. He stroked
his theatrical chin and thought deeply. You see, Alf
has a jazz theory which he says works. He put it like
this to me: 'Can, man, in jazz I sell rhythm. That's
the staple. Sure, now and then I meet a lovely voice
that I can't afford to blind-eye. And it's likely to be
coloured or Indian. But what I deal in is the rhythm
of the African. That's why I put the bulk of my cast
on the stage, most of them Africans, and they give
with the rhythm. There may be a voice, a crooner,
a songbird hugging the mike, but it's the background
of rhythm with which I pound the audience. I don't
waste any time compering. Number comes after
number in incessant, hammering rhythm so that the

whole hall throbs with its thrill.

'But I always felt that I lacked something, some co-ordinating personality to my rhythm. Somebody who could be the drumming heart of my rhythm section as it were. Now when I came back to Jo'burg, and saw Dolly in Township Jazz, says I to myself: "Herb, that's what you want. That Dolly dynamo." And after all, Can, she really belongs to me. I originally trained her for big-time stagecraft.'

After that, I was the least surprised man in the world when Dolly Rathebe announced that she was leaving Township Jazz for African Jazz. She joined other top-line artists, Joyce Confess, Torrid Tandi, Barbara Brown, Hot Dot Masuku and then gave Herb the verve he wanted.

Recently they went on tour to Cape Town and the Western Province and they wowed the Kaapenaartjies. Somehow Dolly was rather sedate during this tour, but that was because she harboured a secret that few people guessed at. But of that anon. Meanwhile, in Johannesburg, new names were cropping up. Names of young girls who were decidedly making a bid for Dolly's crown of queenship over the blues. Miriam Makeba had for quite a while been building up a tidy reputation with the Manhattan Brothers, and that thing of hers called 'Lovely Lies' was causing a stir in America. And that other thing called 'Thula Ndivile' with its doleful wail, 'Andisafun'ukuhamba, ukuhamba noDudu', was breathing down the heartstrings of every teenager. Then that inferno, Thoko 'Shukuma' Thomo was turning the spirituals of the Lo-Six into sessions of all night sinning. Thoko quite frankly and cheekily sold sex on the stage at half-a-crown a man, and the audiences normally rose out of their seats when her skirts went flying. And among the lesser lights were to be found that waif of the townships, spluttering township lingo, *ag* man, Susan Gabashane, man. In the great old stage tradition Susie always gets into trouble. First she was a nobody, a shadow at the doorsteps of recording studios. Then she got on to *Drum's* cover in a lingo love story called *Baby Come Duze.* The next thing I heard was that the boys were stabbing each other like mad over her. Later she had to flee from Jo'burg and its Spoilers. But she sang 'Skanda Mayeza' and she's now to be reckoned with as an up-and-comer. Another of the lesser lights is Johanna Radebe. No, they are not yet real threats to Dolly's crown. Not yet.

The real threat is Dorothy Masuku. There are those who say, not so. Dorothy is already way past Dolly. Well, Dotty can sing but good. Still, I venture to suggest that she doesn't have the personal. y of Dolly. She doesn't exude from the stage like the Doll.

But now for that little secret. After the Cape Town tour with African Jazz, Dolly went back to Port Elizabeth and her Welcome Duru. Many of us thought that she was throwing in the towel, but she had a damned good reason. You see, she's got long, patient, nine months to wait for a little stranger to join Welcome and her. And she and Welcome are planning to tell some priest, 'I do' very soon, and that is the reason why Dolly has been so sedate and unelectric during the Cape Town tour.

On the other hand Alfred Herbert is toying with the idea of taking his African Jazz to Europe. He has been criticised for it. They say his troupe are too imitative of top American stars whom Europe have heard and seen in the first person. What with African Jazz's Satchmo, Eve Boswell, Billy Daniels and so on.

They say Europe wants Africa indigenous. But
Europe surely is also interested in Africa emergent.
And if that's true, Dolly Rathebe will have to go. I
know what Alf Herbert thinks about her talent. I
know that she herself is keen to sell her wares abroad.
Think of it! Dolly Rathebe, ambassadress of song.

Or is that forthcoming baby going to stall or stale
her? I doubt it. I don't think a little event like that
will put off Dolly. Only one thing, Dolly must come
back to Johannesburg. This fabulous, infamous city is
the spiritual and physical home of non-European
jazz. Other cities can play with their high culture or
ballroom dancing. Jo'burg is not that refined. Jo'burg
is jazz. And Dolly being the natural child of jazz will
have to return to Jo'burg. Otherwise she is finished.

Now before I close this talkative series, how about
a final appraisal of Dolly Rathebe, born Josephine
Malatsi. It is true that she has had a tempestuous life.
Men have floated in and out of it, some as gloomy
spectres, some as rogues, some as vital, effervescent
boilers. She has known and lived the violence and
sordidness and stink of township life. She has drunk,
even, and has found *in vino veritas*, the tot of truth.
People have called her all sorts of names, those who
thought they were entitled to cast the first stone. But
somehow none of these things stuck. Out of the mire
has emerged a queen, on the compost heap has grown
a flower to perfume the township air. But there are
moments when we feel her character doesn't matter.
Exactly the moment when she slithers onto the stage
and sings to us. Like the way she has taken life and
given back to it with a vengeance, so has she taken
her screeching audiences and given back to them with
interest. That furry, breath-hot, sexy voice of hers
has soothed away the cares of thousands of concert-

goers countrywide.

If she has been a she-devil, that's because she's a helluva woman!

ZEKE PAST BACHELOR OF ARTS!
CASEY PAST BACHELOR OF HEARTS!

'Zeke, and ye shall find; ask and ye shall be given,' went the ancient words of wisdom. Well, Zeke Mphahlele, *Drum's* fiction editor, sought high honours in education and he found the Master of Arts degree in English with distinction. Hear! Hear! And Moses Casey Motsisi, that great enemy of bride-price for wives — 'Catch me paying lobola!'he said and was given a bride in Durban, guitar-twanging Alpheus Nkosi's sister, Grace. Boo!

But we are really very proud of the achievements of these two oddments on the staff of *Drum*. They represent the high falutin' solid intellectuality (the Brains Department), and the close-to-the-vest sense of humans and sense of humour, that have made *Drum* the live-wire, quick-triggered, high-minded magazine of Africa. You can simply say, 'by men like these!'

When Ezekiel Mphahlele was capped in Pretoria recently for the MA degree, he had travelled a long, sparkling way up the ladder of education, and even now, with his head high as the moon, he is reaching for the stars. He is going for a doctorate. The stirring

story of how Zeke spelled out his spasmodic lessons
on the pasturelands of Pietersburg, how he stood
watch for the police while his mother purveyed
illicit liquor in Marabastad, Pretoria, how he see-
sawed between the bottom and the top of the class in
Pretoria and Johannesburg, how he sweated at
midnight studies to climb his degrees, and ultimately
burst into success — that story is now a South African
classic!

Indeed, Zeke himself is busy at the moment
writing his life-story. Those in the know about such
things say that already the book shows tremendous
promise and will cause quite a sensation when
published. Well, the world and us are simply gasping
to hear from this corner in the inimitable words of
Africa itself. Already Zeke has written stories that
have impressed America and Europe. But his life-
story, *Down Second Avenue*, promises to be greater
than them all.

But Zeke, the prodigy, is one phenomenon. Zeke
the person, absent-mindedly staring at the chance
question you ask him, or indignant over the cant and
sham and pettiness in the thinking of people who
ought to know better, or laughing deliciously at some
joke that reveals somebody's snobbery, mixed-upped-
ness, or stupidity — that's his kind of joke, you know
— that Zeke is another kind of unmathematics!

In a way, he has a vicious streak of malice. For all
his Falstaffian, boisterous *joie de vivre*, for all his
back-slapping, hail-fellow-well-met camaraderie, his
cheerfulness and open-heartedness, Zeke is a hard
man with those who ought to know better. But in a
climate and country where man can be just honest-
to-God uncomplexed, unfrustrated man, there Zeke
will flower out into the pure, unblemished character

that he truly is. Will some day in the future give this
man a break?

And now that irrepressible, fun-loving, humour-
packed, pocket-sized young man, Moses Casey Motsisi.
I swear that I have not known a shred of serious
thought in him, not a hair of politics or philosophy
or economics—er . . . what's that? Even marriage to
that charming doctor's consultant, Grace Nkosi, is a
kind of joke on Casey. But he is so superbly human.
The earthiness about him is refreshing. He joined the
staff of *Drum* Publications in 1954, becoming the
assistant editor of 'Africa'!

During his high school days I used to teach him
English — I heartily apologise for it. But he got by.
He went to Vlakfontein Normal School to train to
be a teacher. They did something to the boy, out
there, for he felt raw about God's whole mismanaged
universe, and he never became a teacher, thank
heavens! After they chucked him out without ceremony, he got his job on *Drum*.

After some time with this firm, the poison seemed
to drain out of him, and he became little Puck, the
mischievous elf. He dreamed up· and contrived into
print, past unwary editors, some of the craziest
articles and stories. There is one joke against him
which has just recently become a joke. Once he wrote
an article on lobola for *Drum,* yelling, 'It's a racket'.
He showed up all the insipidities of the custom and
ended the article by saying scornfully: 'Catch me
paying lobola!' They should have fleeced the arrant
little rascal for his Durban bride!

Casey is not yet old enough to write his own life
story, although he now talks to me, just because
he's married before me, as if to say, 'Papa, I'm a
big man, now.' But I hate to think of life without

Zeke's snorting and Casey's cavorting. Even if the seas
be rough, boys, *Bon Voyage!*

Remembrances

HENRY NXUMALO

One Saturday afternoon Henry Nxumalo, the news editor of *Golden City Post,* set out to Sophiatown to look for me. He didn't find me in. He came three times, but still didn't find me in, curse my roving ways! Then he went to see another reporter friend, Bloke Modisane, and chatted with him into the early evening. Bloke thought that it was getting late, what with the boys outside getting so knife-happy these days, and he urged Henry to go home early, or to put up for the night. But Henry explained that he had a job to do in Newclare, and proposed to go and sleep at his cousin Percy Hlubi's house in Western Township. So at about seven o'clock in the evening, Henry left the 'Sunset Boulevard' — Bloke's home in Sophiatown, and went to Western Township, across the rails.

He must have felt disgracefully dry, because those days just after Christmas were arid, desert-like in the Western Areas. A man just couldn't find a drop. Henry got to Percy's house, and explained to Percy and his wife that he would like to pass the night there. However, he would first like to go to Newclare where he had a job to do. He would return later to sleep. Meanwhile, the man sat talking, whilst the woman prepared a bed for Henry. Before she turned in for the night, she told Henry that when he came back he would probably find them asleep. He shouldn't bother to knock: 'Just open the door and go to your bed.'

Percy looked at the time and noticed that it was close on eleven. He told Henry to postpone his trip to Newclare for the following day. It was so awfully late. 'Never put off for tomorrow what you can do today,' Henry back-fired grinningly. Then he rose and walked out into the warm night. He never came back to the bed prepared for him.

The following morning, Mrs Hlubi rose early to go to work in Krugersdorp. She was a nurse there and she normally took her train at Westbury Station. She set out for work at about a quarter past five that Sunday morning. When she got to a spot where Malotane Street flowed out of Ballenden Avenue like a tributary, she noticed a body lying on the green grass, one shoe off, one arm twisted behind it, the head pressed against the ground, the eyes glazed in sightless death. And bloody wounds all over the head and body. Good heavens, it was Henry Nxumalo! In hysterical frenzy she rushed back home to tell her husband. Percy went to the scene and saw the battered body of his cousin. He got his friend, Mr Vil Nkomo, to inform Henry's employer. He contacted the police. He chartered a car to go and tell Henry's wife — most cheerless of tasks. Then he got someone to go round and tell all the *Drum* boys.

The way I got the news was through the wife of Benjamin Gwigwi Mrwebi. Gwigwi himself was away in Durban with his combo, the Jazz Dazzlers. So Salome, his wife, took it upon herself to inform those of us who were around. She found me still in bed lazing luxuriously after eight o'clock, and she broke the news to me. Stunned, I crawled out of bed and went with her to the spot marked X. There was already a little crowd gathered and from all the streets flowing into Ballenden people were streaming to the spot.

There he lay, the great, gallant Henry Nxumalo who had fought bravely to bare cruelty, injustice and narrow-mindedness, there he lay in the broiling sun, covered by two flimsy rags.

He who had accepted the challenge of life and dedicated himself to fight against the wrongs of mankind, now lay on the roadside, his last battlefield the gutter, his last enemies arrant knaves for whom, even, Henry had raised his trumpet call. And there was a staggered trail of bloody footsteps that told the graphic story of that night's drama. Let us read as best we can the story told in meandering blood.

About a hundred yards from Coronation Hospital there is a little gate. Less than ten yards from that gate is a pool of blood. The first sign of violence. From that pool footsteps made in blood turn in and out towards Western Township, showing how a man, mortally wounded, struggled with his great unyielding spirit to get away. Twenty yards of agonised staggering and the man dropped off the road among the stones. Probably heaving, breathing heavily, he dragged himself up and struggled on . . . and on . . . and on. And the life-blood spurts from him. Ah, a little patch of green grass barely visible. Here might a man rest his gashed body. And he dropped. But the strength ebbed out of him, drip-drip, out of him. He must have fought madly with his heart when he thought of his unfinished work; that book about South Africa he was writing for America — the draft completed, but who could be trusted to give it the final polish? Florence, the wife who had always so patiently waited for him when he was out on his perilous escapades, who will care for her and her children? And that brotherhood of *Drum*-men, who will continue to give them guidance and encouragement? And the life went out of him. So died Henry Nxumalo, 'Mr *Drum*'. Death is lonely even if your dear ones are there to hold a tender hand on your forehead. Death is desolate if you meet it far away from home on the roadside.

And meanwhile the butchers were somewhere wiping off their knives and probably cracking coarse jokes. It was:

'Murder most foul, as in the best it is:
But this most foul, strange, and unnatural.'

But the unknowing still ask, who was this Henry Nxumalo? Henry was born 39 years ago in Port Shepstone. His grandfather, Gqobo, was an ordinary tribal Zulu who died by falling over a cliff. His father, Lazarus, married a transitional Zulu girl, Josephine and they had seven children: Henry, the eldest; Gertie now late; the twins Benjamin, now living in Port Sheptstone, and Daniel, now late; then Zebbar also known as Lance now living in Edenvale; Abigail, late, and Ntombizodwa, also late.

Because their parents died when they were still young, they more or less had to look after themselves. This one fact accounts for the independent spirit in Henry and his surviving brothers. Henry went to school at St Francis, Mariannhill, did his Junior Certificate, but as he was doing Matric his father died and he had to abandon school. He took up a job as a kitchen boy in Durban, but left it because he didn't like it. He came to Johannesburg. He found a job in a boilermaker's shop. In his spare time he wrote poetry for the *Bantu World*.

Later he got a job with the *Bantu World* as a messenger and hung on for three years until he became sports editor. When the war came he joined up and became a sergeant. He went up North and made various friends. The world beyond showed him how other people thought and lived, so when he came back he was a frustrated man. He came back to the *Bantu World* and made extra money by writing for a Negro paper, the *Pittsburgh Courier*. In 1946 he married a young nurse called Florence. He left to work on a gold mine, later did welfare work for the British Empire Service League, and still freelanced for European papers. In 1951 he joined *Drum*.

It was in 1952 when the fabulous character of Mr *Drum* was created. First the idea was a stunt whereby Mr *Drum* would disguise himself and walk through the locations. The first person who could identify him with a copy of *Drum* would win a £5-note. Up to his death many people were still trying to earn a fiver off Henry.

But the idea of a Mr *Drum* had too many tremendous possibilities. The first opportunity came with the famous Bethal story. Farmers were rumoured to be ill-treating their labourers in the Bethal district, and Henry was sent over to investigate as a labourer himself. He came back with a story that shook the whole country. 'Mr *Drum* Goes to Bethal' was the first Mr *Drum* exposure. And from there Henry had set *Drum* on the map.

Henry got himself arrested on the slight offence of not having a night pass, and he went to jail. His experiences in jail made a chilling story that caused an international sensation. Just about this time a friend of mine reading that story in *Drum* said to me: 'This Mr *Drum* fellow is going bang into history.'

He regarded himself as a contemporary social historian.

Yes, why the bloody hell did they have to choose to murder him? I cannot hide my bitterness at all. But, dear Henry, Mr *Drum* is not dead. Indeed, even while you lived, others were practising the game of Mr *Drum*. Now, we shall take over where you left off. We want you, as you look down on us from among the angels, to mutter: 'The boys sure make a good job of that game, and looks like they might get the world a little cleaner from what I left it.' Bye now.

THE BOY WITH THE TENNIS RACKET

Someone had passed the buck to me. The story went out that a razor-sharp journalist from Durban was coming to Johannesburg to work in our main office. The editor had told someone to find accommodation for him, and that someone had decided that his initiation was best in my hands. In those days handing an other-town boy into my hands for initiation was subtlest excruciation. Not that we would persecute him, we only sought to divest him of the naivetés and extraneous moralities with which we knew he would be encumbered.

He came, I remember, in the morning with a suitcase and a tennis racket — ye gods, a tennis racket! We stared at him. The chaps on *Drum* at that time had fancied themselves to be poised on a dramatic, implacable kind of life. Journalism was still new to most of us and we saw it in the light of the heroics of Henry Nxumalo, decidedly not in the light of tennis, which we classed with draughts.

He had a puckish, boyish face, and a name something like Nathaniel Nakasa. We soon made it Nat. I took him to Sophiatown and showed him the room where he would stay — what was it? Three minutes, five minutes? Then I took him to my shebeen in Edith Street.

There was a beautiful girl there, and I hoped Nat would make her. As a matter of cold fact, as he declined drink after drink, I decided that he was interested. She was Tswana and he Zulu, but they got on swimmingly, love being polyglot. Honest, I don't know how it happened, but I left him there. He told me later, that a few tsotsis came in and he approached them with trepidated terror. He asked them if they knew where Can Themba lived and they immediately looked hostile. (At first, they thought he contemplated some harm to the revered Can Themba.) But when Mpho, the girl, explained that this was really a friend of the chap, who had deserted him there in one of his drunken impulses, they said, 'O.K. Durban-boy, hang around and we'll take you there.'

This is a measure of Nat's character. He was in a new situation. He knew about Jo'burg tsotsis, the country's worst. He was scared — he told me later he was. But he went with them, chatted with them, wanted to know what type of character this, his host, was. Though he got only grunts, it was the journalist in action, not the terrified fish out of water.

He found me at home, out of this world's concerns. Later, he found out about Jo'burg without the aid of my derelictions. He quickly learned about the united nations of Fordsburg and Malay Camp; about the liberal enclaves in Hillbrow; about the cosmopolitanism of Johannesburg. Also about the genuine values in those people who were not trying to prove or protest anything: God knows South Africa begs any stranger to want to prove or protest something, and Johannesburg is its Mecca.

But Nat sought for something inside himself that would make language with the confused environment in which he now existed. He sought, fought, struggled, argued, posed — but I doubt if he found it. The South African stubbornness was too much for him, and he had to go into exile.

The bitterest commentary on South Africa is typified by Nat. All those Africans who want to be loyal, hard-working, intelligent citizens of the country are crowded out. They don't want to bleach themselves, but they want to participate and contribute to the wonder that the country can become. They don't want to be fossilised into tribal inventions that are no more real to them than they would have been to their forefathers.

Nat's was such a voice. Sobukwe's is that of protest and resistance. Casey Motsisi's that of derisive laughter. Bloke Modisane's that of implacable hatred. Ezekiel Mphahlele's that of intellectual contempt. Nimrod Mkele's that of patient explanation to be patient. Mine, that of self-corrosive cynicism. But Nat told us, 'There must be humans on the other side of the fence; it's only we haven't learned how to talk.'

We replied, 'Humans? Not enough.'

One day, we met at a dry cleaners called the Classic. Nat bought the drinks and said he had an idea. Ideas were sprouting all over the place, but any excuse for a drink was good enough.

After the ninth we got around to discussing the idea. Nat proposed starting a really good, artistic magazine. He wanted all of us — I don't mean just those non-White journalists present — but all of us: black, white, coloured, Indian. For want of superior inspiration we decided to call the damned thing *The Classic* — the place where it was conceived, born, and most of the time bred. Most of us got stinkingly drunk, but Nat captained the boat with a level head and saw to it that we met deadline.

He slipped into the artistic-intellectual set of Hillbrow and I had to go there. In between he met a girl who seemed to match the accomplishments he sought. She was African (that would vindicate him from the slur that any white woman was better than every black woman, though I think Nat would have thought of this with contempt); she was educated and intelligent (though I think Nat was no snob); she was lively and interesting (though I think Nat would have none of a floozie); she could mix with the High, the Middle and the Low (Nat chose what he wanted from High, Middle and Low). Eventually, she eclipsed herself and went to marry someone in Europe.

Nat had a brother here in Swaziland, Joe Nakasa. One day Joe took me to Chesterville in Durban to meet his family. There was a father, a sister and a brother. Another brother was in England studying at Cambridge. Their mother was in Sterkfontein mental hospital, unable to recognize even her sons. Nat talked little about his mother, but once when I had gone there with him, he broke out into bitter, scalding tears. I had not been there when he saw his mother, but I guessed that it was a gruelling, cruel experience.

Then he went to America. We thought this was the big break.

At the time of his death, Nat was planning interesting things, journalistically speaking, interesting things . . . . *Quo vadis?*

Proemdra

MUSIC, FOOD OF LOVE!
tale of a girl whom music saved from the blues

first day: Friday
I was walking along, minding my business, when I saw two people looking out of two windows in the same house . . . so a drama began.

Through the one window I saw the girl reading a letter. It was a very sad story that letter told her for the tears rolled down.

It gave her the blues so that long into the night she brooded over the guy who had jilted her and written: 'I want you no more.'

Then suddenly during the night she started up as the soft moaning notes of a saxophone broke through to her in delicious despair.

Next door, a new arrival was rehearsing his blues on his horn for a forthcoming concert, unknowing what effect he was having.

on Saturday
And the next night as she took her bath she heard him again and the wailing music seeped into her soul, rhapsodising all of her.

He poured his whole life into it, all the yearning and desire for achievement he had felt in his youth, went into his sax.

And as he came out she rushed to her window to see the man who so much had suffered from life or love, so much spilled his soul.

on Saturday night
So the same night she made herself up for him, hoping she would contrive a chance to meet him, charm him, net him for herself.

And when he came home she hurried forward to open the door for him. She warmly welcomed him with her breezy smile of invitation.

In her room she made him play for her, play out his soul, and it became a sweet night of musical love as he set her heart on fire.

on Sunday
They fell in love on sunshine Sunday and they discovered a new beautiful world in each other, a new dynamic reason for living.

They tumbled into each other's arms in their thrilling to the magic and wonder of new delirious love, and the first kiss.

So out they went, a-loving and a-trusting each other,
unafraid of the hard, cruel world waiting outside for
young people in love.

PART THREE

From The House of Truth

THE BOTTOM OF THE BOTTLE

Comes a time when a man feels that everything in his personal organisation cannot go on as before for much longer. No dramatic decision may be taken in some bursting hour of change. But all the same, a man may feel that those in their bits of rag who have for so long been meekly begging at the gate of his mind can no longer be joked or carefully drunk away.

I remember well one of those days during my bottle blindness in Sophiatown. We were in the House of Truth — my room at 111 Ray Street, Sophiatown, Johannesburg — I and all those young frustrated Africans who flitted through the half-legal life of the urban African in the Union.

They were all there that day. Philip, the Health Inspector, who had been with me at Fort Hare; Peter, his younger brother, who was annually being baulked of Matriculation by the requirements of a supplementary examination in that malevolent subject, English (Higher Grade); Oubaas, the timeless one, who read morbid things like *The Inferno, Paradise Lost,* and *Dr Faustus;* Maxie, scared stiff of two fingers of brandy, but obsessed with impressing the girls; the Kabaka (so

called because his uncle once exiled him from home
for his shiftlessness); Jazz-boy, miniature like the
saxophone that brought him girls, liquor and an
occasional beating-up. And I, their host.

The table was spired with bottles of brandy, gin
and beer; and we were at the stage of high discourse,
much like the majestic demons in the burning pit.

For a moment, as I looked at those young men
around me, the luxury of a mild flood of conscience
swept over me. They had all at one time or another
had visions: to escape their environment; to oppose
and overcome their context; to evade and out-
distance their destiny by hard work and sacrifice, by
education and native ability, by snatching from the
table of occupation some of the chance crumbs of the
high-chaired culture. Lord, it struck me, what a
treasury of talent I had here in front of me. Must
they bury their lives with mine like this under a load
of Sophiatown bottles?

I say it was conscience that struck me, because I
knew that many of them looked up to me, my way
of life, and repeated my despair and its defences
behind my back. I knew that they were excited by
me when I said, 'Why should one believe in anything
when one could live — live, gentlemen, at 212 degrees
Fahrenheit? The trouble is, gentlemen, for me,
human nature stinks; but that is all the material we
have to work with.' They said these things I said. But
never with my own deep sense of doubt, the sleepless,
tossing suspicion that often made me itch in the very
heat of my enthusiasms.

I think the rest of African society looked upon us
as an excrescence. We were not the calm dignified
African that the Church so admires (and fights for);
not the unspoiled rural African the Government so

admires, for they tell no lies, they do not steal, and above all, they do not try to measure up to the white man. Neither were we tsotsis in the classical sense of the term, though the tsotsis saw us as cousins. I swear, however, that not one of the gentlemen who associated with me in that period was guilty (caught or not) of murder, rape, assault, robbery, theft, or anything like that. True, we spent nights at police stations, but it was invariably for possession of illicit liquor or, its corollary, drunkenness. We were not 'cats', either; that sophisticated group of urban Africans who play jazz, live jazz and speak the township transmigrations of American slang.

We were those sensitive might-have-beens who had knocked on the door of white civilisation (at the highest levels that South Africa could offer) and had heard a gruff 'No' or a 'Yes' so shaky and insincere that we withdrew our snail horns at once.

An incident that Oubaas related to us illustrates this 'Yes'. He had been working for a white man of truly untraditional generosity of spirit. This boss allowed Oubaas to drive his car on private jaunts, to share lunch with him, to visit his house for a drink. Sometimes Oubaas even brought him into the nether world of the township where he liked the abandon of its denizens. And his politics? Positively anti-white, if not altogether subversive! They were back-slapping buddies, Oubaas and his boss.

Then one day there came into the shop — a chemist's — an old white lady. She gave her order, and it turned into quite a fair sized parcel. The old lady wanted to carry her parcel to her car but the boss would have nothing of it. The old lady insisted that she could manage. And the boss insisted . . . .

'Don't worry, my boy will carry it out for you.

That's what I hired the native for.'

'Boy' and 'native' are hardly terms used in respectable race relations society. Something in the white man's intonation makes these innocuous words feel like barbed wire across a bare back.

Oubaas, normally not ungallant, was furious. But, for us, the joke was on Oubaas. He did not walk out on that nice boss at once, but went on working for him long months afterwards.

But for the most we savoured of life pungently. Living precariously, cheekily confronting the world's challenges. I, for myself, deliberately cocooned my mind away from the stirrings around it. 1948, the Nationalists took over power in South Africa. 1949, the Youth League forced their Programme of Action into African National Congress policy. 1952, the Defiance of Unjust Laws Campaign was launched. 1955, the Freedom Charter was proclaimed. 1956, the massive Treason Arrests took place in pre-dawn raids. 1960, Sharpeville! Colossal shadows of huge, angry politicians fell upon and affrighted us. Something there was that thundered in the skies.

Yet nightly we repaired to the House of Truth, swinging bottles of brandy filched from the dark cellars where the white man hid his courage from us, and drank ourselves cold.

By this time it was becoming clear to me that I was really fighting something inside that nibbled at my soaked soul. Yet, what the hell! We were cavaliers of the evanescent, romantics who turned the revolt inwards upon our own bruised spirits. It was flight now, no more just self-erasure.

Something happened one night that made me sit up and think. We had been drinking as usual, and the casualties were lying all over my room: on the bed,

over the studio couch, sprawled across the floor. I
was sitting at the table, with a half-full bottle in my
hand, and trying to make a floozie who was too far-
out to distinguish Cupid from Dr Verwoerd. Then
there came a knock on the door. I reeled over to open
it and admit two very well-known politicians. The
one was a shadow of a shadow with that lean and
hungry look, but it was the other, bulkier man who
really blurred through my half-consciousness.

He was huge and shaped like a barrel whose oblong
began at the knees. He had arms like distorted
Zeppelins with Russian sausage fingers at their ends.
His face ballooned at you as he breathed, and that
face was black for you, willfully black.

He spoke in a voice that was eternally hoarse.

'Can Themba, we'd like to talk to you,' he grated.

I motioned them into seats which they took like
senators.

He wasted no time. 'Look,' he said, 'the fight is
on. We know that you're not a membah, but this
fight is for Ahfrich. We want you all, nice-time boys'
— here he looked at me accusingly — 'tsotsis, teachers,
businessmen, lawyers, doctors, all! The Ahfrican
Nahtional Congress is not a political party, it is the
organisation of every Ahfrican, every Ahfrican.'

'But how do you know what I think?' I parried.

'Man,' came the lean man impatiently, 'you're
black, are you not? You're an African, are you not?
So long as you're black we know what you suffer and
what you think.'

'I see,' said I, evasively. 'What is it you want me to
do?'

'We want your support, man,' said the big one
aghast at this political moron. 'We hear that you've
got some young men about you, and you can make

them do things, do things that we don't think are in the nahtional interest. Will you be with us?'

I jerked up my thumb automatically and barked, 'Afrika!'

'Mayibuuuye!' they rasped.

They had risen at the salute, and nearly upset the table. My bottle was staggering, but I caught it swiftly. I served a glass and offered them some, but they refused. I gulped my drink down so that the tears came to my eyes.

'So you are with us?' asked the big man as they prepared to go.

'Sure,' I said, 'sure,' hugging my beloved bottle.

But as they went out, I fancy I heard the lean one muttering, 'He's drunk, that's all.'

After that, perhaps largely because I paid more attention, I heard more and more *politics:* bitter, heady, virulent stuff. It expressed, in venomous terms, the wrath of a people who had come to the damn-it-all threshold. Also, the despair of a people tied helplessly to an ant-heap: it was savage swearing. What struck me more those days was the great number of ordinary folk who spoke politics.

The machine that was ploughing up the country could not leave one square inch undisrupted. In Zeerust, Sekhukhuniland, Pondoland, official policies were driving the tribesmen to resistance.

That was odd. Hitherto, the bad boys had been the urban Africans. They were spoiled', tried to imitate the white man, were the targets of agitators, Communists and tsotsis and, above all, a sore to the segregationist faith of our masters by their insolent infiltration into the holy preserves of whitedom; they were the *black peril*, the direct descendants of the treacherous *impis* under Dingaan, if you can take the contradiction.

But, increasingly now, our all-tolerant country brothers rose up against the authorities, not in lawlessness, but because the Government's policy of retribalisation rode rough-hooves over tribal custom and degraded the true position of the chief.

The tribal areas showed clearly that there had once been an ordered peaceful system by which tribes were able to live. It was a system of society and government that Africans knew to belong to their own customary sense of justice and what was proper. The shadiest nuance of interpretation in the *Kgotla* (Tribal Council) could lead to spirited argument where even the chief could be required to explain his innovations. For the chief, too, was bound by custom.

With all its limitations, this other world composition served the needs of the times. It merged with the simple economy; it expressed the tribal psychology; slowly, with patient humour, it absorbed the wisdom and the philosophy of the fire-place — but it was so made that it could roar into violence at a moment's blowing.

The institutions of a system like this — a system that served the needs so well — could not just die, even with the change of times. They just adapted themselves by natural differentiation to new requirements. And the genuine ones among them asserted a new influence in an even more dynamic environment. The witchdoctor's craft survives in the most revolutionary politics. The principle of *free debate* attends every discussion of significance, the women exert their oblique, but very effective, influence on every project of importance.

But our old-world tribal state was not to be left *virgo intacta*. The fifteenth century hurled at us the

economic and adventurous restlessness of Europe,
and subsequently the mania called the 'Scramble for
Africa' shuddered the sub-continent. The sheer
physical impact of the assault was enough to stagger
the edifice of tribalism. I can almost see my infinitely
great-grandfather, leaping to his feet on a rock and
gaping at a sailing ship seeking harbour — all his
patriarchal dignity forgotten, as he exclaims, 'Hay!'

Yet these white men did not just bring things of
wonder: the floating house, the booming stick, the
gaudy beads. They also brought ideas — evil, good,
indifferent — ideas such as could subvert and demolish
our tribal system. Funny, the idea with which they
impressed us most was not Justice or Love Thy
Neighbour or Liberty, Fraternity and Equality or
Live and Let Live — no, simply, 'You acquire a right
to a right only by force.' And they are still busy,
through the centuries, trying to live down that
spectacular bit of basic education. For us, it is only
recently that sugar-coated slogans have been needed
to cover that profound 'truth' of Western, civilised
morality.

But then we were barbarians both.

The ideas did their bit, but it was only when our
labour was needed that a deliberate drive was made to
haul us from our tribal havens to come out to work.
And where tribalism did not help to demonstrate the
dignity of labour, tribalism had to be smashed. They
were so bloody successful that now they fear they
have drawn too many of us into the fields of urban
industry and have sired themselves a problem.

Of course, some semblance of tribal integrity
remained in the Reserves, but the migrant labour
system made a pretty delinquent bastard out of it.
Men came to the mines for a spell, lived in compounds

and soured the city only in hectic excursions, then went back to awe their homekeeping brethren, or to dismay their chiefs and elders with their outlandish ways.

But tribalism was crumbling all over and the Africans were fast becoming a race of city-dwellers, with snatched visits to the Reserves. Hard economic and social laws dictated that these people would seek to adjust themselves into some form of permanence and security and, in the process, demand the conditions that would facilitate such adjustment.

Somewhere near this point, the authorities decided that the whole process of African urbanisation should be repudiated as a policy if not altogether as a fact, let the skies crack! And the simple method projected was the retribalisation of the people and the re-establishment of the authority of the chiefs — at least, that is, those chiefs who would keep their noses clean and obey the Government. And where tribal custom did not suit — for tribal custom chooses its own chiefs in its own way — well, who the hell is running the show, after all?

Meantime, however, other things had happened.

Largely because of the efforts of the African National Congress, but to as large an extent because of the industrial and population changes in the country and the excessive emphasis of white politics on *colour*, Africans were everywhere debunking tribalism and comtemplating each other as *Africans*, themselves as a *nation* — whatever the guide-books of the State Information Office say.

And this African view of themselves does not confine itself to South African blacks. It identifies itself with all the black people of Africa; it breathes out the African Personality; it palpitates in time with

the heartbeats of Accra. It strives hard to make itself
vacuum enough to receive the winds of change from
the North. And against this there is nothing to
engender a peculiar South African loyalty: not a
black middle class; not a stake in the land, its wealth,
or, for that matter, its law, order and good government; nothing to make enough of them hesitate at
the contemplation of this country's destruction.

The conflict between the opposing forces seems
inevitable: the (roughly) white nationalism poised
before the (not too roughly) black nationalism. The
dilemma is so complete!

As I brood over these things, I, with my insouciant
attitude to matters of weight, I feel a sickly despair
which the most potent bottle of brandy cannot wash
away. What can I do?

REQUIEM FOR SOPHIATOWN

Realism can be star-scattering, even if you have lived your whole unthinking life in reality. Especially in Sophiatown, these days, where it can come with the sudden crash of a flying brick on the back of your head.

Like the other day when Bob Gosani and I sneaked off to our secret shebeen in Morris Street. We were dodging an old friend of ours whom we call the Leech, for he is one of those characters who like their drink — any amount — so long as someone else pays for it.

Well, this secret shebeen in Morris Street was a nice place. You take a passage through Meyer Street over haphazard heaps of bricks where houses have been broken down, you find another similar passage that leads you from Ray Street into Edith Street where you find yet another passage but neater, having always been there, between the coloured school and Jerusalem-like slum-houses. You go down a little, and suddenly there it is.

Quite a fine place, too. A little brick wall, a minute garden of mostly Christmas flowers, a half-veranda (the other half has become a little kitchen) and the floor of the veranda polished a bright green.

Inside, the sitting-room may be cluttered with furniture, it is so small, but you sink comfortably into a sofa as one of the little tables that can stand under the other's belly is placed before you, and you place your order. Half-a-jack of brandy!

How often have Bob and I not whooped happily: 'Yessus! the Leech will never find us here.' So, though there were more direct routes to this place, we always took the passages. They say these people can smell when you are going to have a drink.

But that day, as we emerged into Morris Street, it was as if that brick had just struck us simultaneously on our heads. That sweet little place was just not there. Where it should have been was a grotesque, grinning structure of torn red brick that made it look like the face of a mauled boxer trying to be sporting after his fight. A nausea of despair rose up in me, but it was Bob who said the only appropriate thing: 'Shucks.'

Here is the odd thing about Sophiatown. I have long been inured to the ravages wreaked upon Sophiatown. I see its wrecks daily, and through many of its passages that have made such handy short-cuts for me, I have frequently stepped gingerly over the tricky rubble. Inside of me, I have long stopped arguing the injustice, the vindictiveness, the strong arm authority of which prostrate Sophiatown is a conspicuous symbol.

Long ago I decided to concede, to surrender to the argument that Sophiatown was a slum, after all. I am itchingly nagged by the thought that slum-clearance should have nothing to do with the theft of free-hold rights. But the sheer physical fact of Sophiatown's removal has intimidated me.

Moreover, so much has gone — veritable institutions. Fatty of the Thirty-nine Steps. Now, that was a great shebeen! It was in Good Street. You walked up a flight of steps, the structure looked dingy as if it would crash down with you any moment. You opened a door and walked into a dazzle of bright electric light, contemporary furniture, and massive Fatty. She was a legend. Gay, friendly, coquettish, always ready to sell you a drink. And that mama had everything: whisky, brandy, gin, beer, wine — the lot. Sometimes she could even supply cigars. But now that house is flattened. I'm told that in Meadowlands she has lost the zest for the game. She has even tried to look for work in town. Ghastly.

Dwarf, who used to find a joke in everything. He used to walk into Bloke's place, and catch us red-handed playing the music of Mozart. He would cock his ear, listen a little and in his gravel voice comment: 'No wonder he's got a name like that.' There is nothing that Dwarf loved more than sticking out his tongue to a cop and running for it. I once caught him late at night in his Meadowlands house washing dishes. He still manfully tries to laugh at himself.

And Mabeni's, where the great Dolly Rathebe once sang the blues to me. I didn't ask her. She just sidled over to me on the couch and broke into song. It was delicious. But now Dolly is in Port Elizabeth, and Mabeni, God knows where.

These are only highlights from the swarming, cacophonous, strutting, brawling, vibrating life of the Sophiatown that was. But it was not all just shebeeny, smutty, illegal stuff. Some places it was such as dreams are made of.

I am thinking of those St Cyprian's schoolboys.

who a decade ago sweatingly dug out the earth behind the house of the Community of the Resurrection, in order to have a swimming pool. It still stands, and the few kids left still paddle in it. Some of those early schoolboys of St Cyprian's later went up to Father Ross or Father Raynes or Father Huddlestone who wangled a bursary for them to go to St Peter's, then on to Fort Hare, and later even Wits, to come back doctors.

Their parents, patiently waiting and working in town, skimped a penny here, a tickey there, so that they might make the necessary alteration to their house, or pay off the mortgage. And slowly Sophiatown was becoming house-proud.

Of course, there were pressures too heavy for them. After the war, many people came to Johannesburg to seek work and some hole to night in. As they increased, they became a housing problem. As nobody seemed to care, they made Sophiatown a slum.

But the children of those early Sophiatonians — some of them are still around. It is amazing how many of them are products of the Anglican Mission at St Cyprian's. I meet them often in respectable homes, and we talk the world to tatters.

Mostly we talk of our lot in life. After all, too often we have been told that we are the future leaders of our people. We are the young stalwarts who are supposed to solve the problems of our harassed world.

'Not political unity we need,' one will say. 'Our society is too diverse and unwieldy for that. Just a dynamic core of purified fighters with clear objectives and a straightforward plan of action. That is all.'

Another: 'No! we must align ourselves with the

new forces at play in Africa today. There already is the dynamism. The idea of a one Africa has never been put as powerfully as at Accra recently. You see, Africans, wherever they are, have not a territorial, a local loyalty: they don't feel that they belong to a South Africa or a Federation or a Tanganyika or a Kenya or a West Africa; but with Africans in the whole of Africa. In fact, many of us are wondering if Arabs and Egyptians are also Africans. They probably are.'

Still another: 'But if the boys in the North are getting busy, shouldn't we start something here ourselves?'

'Waal, you see, our ANC here has been caught with its pants down. The Africanists are claiming that Accra has proclaimed their stand. And the ANC representative there could only discuss the tactical difficulties of the ANC in South Africa with her special conditions.'

'Ya. But this African Personality idea, what does it mean to us? What does it mean, anyway?'

'I'll tell you. In the world today are poised against each other two massive ideologies: of the East and of the West. Both of them play international politics as if we're bound to choose between them. Between them only. We have just discovered that we can choose as we like, if we grow strong in our own character. But there's more to this. The West has had a damned long time to win us. Win us over to Western thinking. Western Christian way of living. Their ideas of democracy and their Christian ideals were wonderful, but they did not mean them.

'Let me explain. We are quite a religious people. We accept the idealism of Christianity. We accept its high principles. But in a stubborn, practical sense we

believe in reality. Christian Brotherhood must be real.
Democracy must actually be the rule of the people:
not of a white hobo over a black M A.

'To us, if a witchdoctor says he'll bring rain, we
not only want to see the rain fall, but also the crops
sprout from the earth. That's what a rainmaker's for,
nay? If the bone-thrower says he'll show up the
bastard who's been slinging lightning at me, I expect
him to swing that bolt of lightning right back. So if
the priest says God's on my side, I'd like to see a few
more chances and a little less white man's cursing.

'But, in any case, Christianity is now an anaemic
religion. It cannot rouse the ancient in me — especially
the Chaka instinct I still have. Now, you and I are
educated guys. We don't go for the witchcraft stuff.
And we don't want to go for the juke-box stuff. But
much as we deny it, we still want the thrill of the wild
blood of our forefathers. The whites call it savagery.
Ineradicable barbarism. But in different degrees we
want the colour and vigour and vibrant appeal of it
all. So the tsotsi seeks in the cowboy the way to strut
across the streets with swaying hips and a dangerous
weapon in each hand. So the Zionist thumps his drum
and gyrates his holy fervour up the streets. So you
and I and these guys here discuss politics, teasingly
dancing around the idea of violence.

'All it means is that in wanting to express her
demand for democratic self-determination, Africa is
also releasing her ancientmost desire to live life over
the brim. That's how come we sometimes seem to
talk in two voices.'

'Wait a minute,' another shrieks, 'wait a minute.
We're not all like that. Some of us would like to get
things right, and start anew. Some piece of social
engineering could get things working right, if our

moral purposes were right, not just vengeful.'

'Sure but our masters have taught this damned thing, violence, so well by precept — often practice — that they get you to believe that it's the only way to talk turkey to them.'

We do not only talk about this particular subject. Our subjects are legion. Nkrumah must be a hell of a guy, or is he just bluffing? What about our African intellectuals who leave the country just when we need them most? But is it honestly true that we don't want to have affairs with white girls? What kind of white supremacy is this that cannot stand fair competition? What will happen if a real topmost Nat gets caught by the Immorality Act? In fact, all those cheeky questions that never get aired in public.

But it always ends up with someone saying, 'Aw shut up, folks, you got no plan to liberate us.'

Somewhere here, and among a thousand more individualistic things, is the magic of Sophiatown. It is different and itself. You don't just find your place here, you make it and you find yourself. There's a tang about it. You might now and then have to give way to others making their ways of life by methods not in the book. But you can't be bored. You have the right to listen to the latest jazz records at Ah Sing's over the road. You can walk a coloured girl of an evening down to the Odin Cinema, and no questions asked. You can try out Rhugubar's curry with your bare fingers without embarrassment. All this with no sense of heresy. Indeed, I've shown quite a few white people 'the little Paris of the Transvaal' — but only a few were Afrikaners.

What people have thought to be the brazenness of Sophiatown has really been its clean-faced frankness. And, of course, its swart jowl against the rosy cheek of Westdene.

Ay, me. That was the Sophiatown that was.

I shall have to leave these respectable homes of my friends and stumble over the loose bricks back to my den. I hear tell that Blackie is still about in his shack behind the posh house in devastated Millar Street.

Blackie's landlord is still facing it out, what the hell for? Since the Rathebe case most of the standholders have decided to capitulate. They are selling out, like rats letting the passengers sink. Solly got caught in this — the newest racket. His landlord told him nothing. Waited for him to pay the next month's rent, although he knew that he was planning to sell out. The Resettlement Board has been very sympathetic with such cases; it has told tenants not to pay landlords rent any more, for they may suddenly be given yesterday's notice and the GG will come to break down the house over their heads.

Solly was not at home when the landlord trekked. When he got there he found his furniture was left outside and a policeman was guarding the house. Poor Solly had to rush about looking for some place to put his stuff for the night. Half-a-dozen friends helped.

And still I wander among the ruins trying to find one or two of the shebeens that Dr Verwoerd has overlooked. But I do not like the dead eyes with which some of these ghost houses stare back at me. One of these days I, too, will get me out of here. Finish and klaar!